Discover English

Frequently Asked Questions For Adults

What is this book about?

Discover English is in level one of the *Practise & Pass 11+* series. It's a workbook for students who are going to take an 11+ test or school entrance exam that includes an English section. In it I introduce students to the five key areas of English – spelling, sentence structure, punctuation, grammar and comprehension – provide examples of the key question types they'll typically face in the exams, and give them 280 original questions to practise.

I provide coaching for students *throughout* the book. I talk them through the whole process, from answering questions to helping them understand their mistakes, so they gain a firm understanding of the basics.

How do I use this book?

The book is divided into bite-sized lessons for the student to work through. Each lesson covers a specific area in English.

For spelling, sentence structure and punctuation the lessons are set up in the same way.

1. I explain the question type, giving the student an understanding of what they need to know.
2. I provide a worked example or two to show how the question type is best tackled.

   (Note: I do recommend that an adult reads through the explanation and example(s) with the student to ensure they have a firm understanding of what is required.)
3. When ready, the student should work through the first set of practice questions on their own.
4. The answers to the questions are given on the following page. Once the student has completed the practice questions they can mark their answers themselves.
5. At the end of the answers I provide a summary of what the student's score means and give them hints on how to improve it, if necessary.

   (Note: the student should discuss any errors and talk through the hints together with an adult so that any problems can be dealt with straight away.)
6. Next there is a second set of practice questions. Again, I suggest that the student shouldn't work on these until they understand why they made mistakes first-time around.

   Important: this second set of questions should be marked by an adult and the answers can be found on pages 127 and 128. You might want to cut these out of the book so the temptation for the student to take a peek is removed!

For grammar and comprehension the lessons are set out slightly differently – after the explanation and worked example there is one set of practice questions which tests both disciplines at the same time. The answers here should be marked by an adult.

Finally, there is a score sheet at the back of the book which should be completed after each lesson to keep a record of progress. This can be used to identify the question types the student needs to practise more.

(Note: occasionally I will include a question that hasn't been explained in the lesson. This is by design: the student will very likely come up against a question they are not familiar with in the actual test so it's important that they get used to applying the knowledge they have to work out the right answer.)

Why does this book feature multiple choice answers?

Multiple choice answers are becoming the most common format for the 11+. This means that four or five possible answers are given for each question and they are presented to the student in a grid format. To answer the question correctly the student has to put a horizontal line in the empty box next to the correct answer.

- It's important that students learn to use these answer grids correctly from the outset so they can avoid making common errors, such as marking the wrong box or accidentally missing out questions.
- You must make sure you find out from the examination centre whether the multiple choice format will be used in the final exam, so you're confident that the student is doing the right preparation.

When should the student start to prepare for the exam and how often should they practise?

The sooner the student starts to prepare for the exam the better. Realistically, I suggest there should be a full year's run-up to the test so the student has a chance to practice all of the subject areas and question types that may appear in the exam without having to study for hours and hours each week. This means working through all three levels of the *Practise & Pass 11+* series (this book is in level one of the series) at a steady and realistic pace.

For this book I recommend students work at the pace of one lesson a week, which means 16 weeks in total. However, if a student is able there is nothing to stop them moving through the book at a quicker pace.

What's the best way for a student to study?

- It's important that the student gets used to a test-type environment – this means making sure there's a clear space to work in, with no distractions. All TVs and music need to be switched off, the student should be sat at a table and there should be a clock in clear view so they can time themselves.
- Students should use a pencil to answer the questions and have an eraser and some scrap paper to hand which they can use for any workings out.

  (Note: I highly recommend that the student avoid practising on the same days that they have school homework and that they also have other extra-curricular activities to do – this means they have other outlets for their energies and don't become overworked, stressed, or too bored with the practice.)

How quickly should a student answer the questions?

I have suggested timings for each lesson but do note that, as this book is in level one of the series, the timings here are more generous than they will be in the actual exam. At this stage students should concentrate on becoming familiar with the question types and their methods – they can ignore the timings for the time-being if they wish.

Once students are used to the questions they can then practise speeding up. At level two of the series I do expect the students to get up to speed and they should follow the timings far more closely (this way they are prepared to work at a 'real time' pace that matches the actual exam).

What score should the student be aiming for?

Remember that 11+ tests and entrance exams are tough to pass. I have written this book to reflect that fact, so it's unlikely that the student will sail through the book scoring 100% in each lesson!

After the first set of practice questions in every lesson I have given a target score for that particular question type – this is based on my experience of teaching them year on year and will help you assess how the student is doing, and which areas, if any, need work. I also include helpful tips on how students can improve, and would recommend they make use of the 'vocabulary builders'.

I should add that the scores here in no way indicate whether the student will definitely pass or fail the exam; they are here only as a guide.

What are the 'vocabulary builders'?

There are two vocabulary builder exercises in this book. These are extra tasks to help improve the student's vocabulary. In addition to these, one of the best ways for students to help prepare for the examination is to read regularly. The better their vocabulary, the better they are likely to cope with the questions in the actual exam.

What should I do once this book is completed?

This book is just the start; I would recommend that the student move on to level two of the series: *Develop English*. In level two there are many more practice questions covering more question types and trickier versions of questions that stretch the student further and improve their familiarity with what's expected from them. There is also further advice from me on how students can improve their scores and speed up their work, ensuring they are fully prepared for test day.

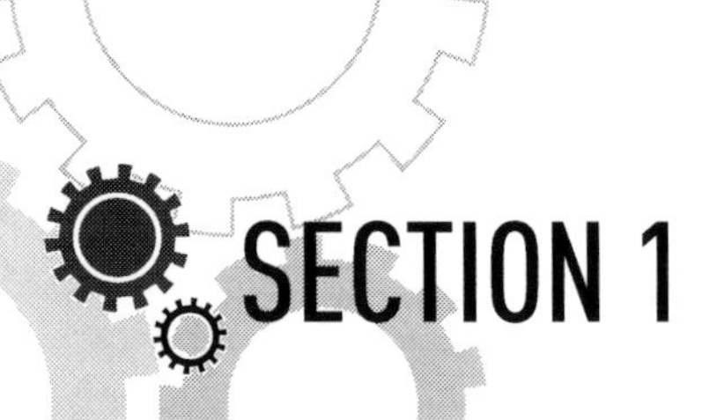

SECTION 1

LESSON 1 Improving Your Spelling Skills

In this exercise you'll be looking for words that are spelled incorrectly or are misused. You'll need to pay close attention as there are words that are pronounced in the same way but are spelled differently and mean different things. To use the correct word you must understand the context in which it is used in the sentence. A clue to help you remember the correct meaning and usage has been given where appropriate. Let's look at some examples.

Word	Meaning	Clue
there	As in 'Over there', 'There it is'.	Take off the first letter and the word spells 'here' – these are both words that refer to location: 'here' and 'there'.
their	It belongs to them – 'It is their turn'.	Remove the first letter and the word is 'heir' – someone who inherits something so it belongs to them.
they're	'They are' becomes 'They're' as in 'They're happy'.	When you see an apostrophe like this it indicates two words have been combined – in this case 'they' and 'are'. See lesson 7 for more information on apostrophes.
here	As in 'Over Here', 'Here it is'.	See 'there' above.
hear	Hearing a sound – 'I can hear some music.'	Remember this rhyme – 'You hear with your ear' – remove the first letter and you get 'ear'.
where	As a question or indicating a place – 'Where are you?', 'She was where she said she would be.'	
wear	When wearing an item of clothing – 'He wears expensive shoes.'	
ware	Something that is sold – 'The merchants were selling their wares in the market.'	Not a common word – think of a 'warehouse' as a place where goods are stored before they are sold.
your	It belongs to you – 'Please answer your mobile phone.'	Remove the last letter and it spells 'you'. So it belongs to you.
you're	'You are' becomes 'You're' as in 'You're not allowed to go in there.'	Again watch out for the apostrophe that indicates two words have been combined.

Make sure you have learned the spellings above before you try the practice questions.

Now, here's an example question. Read the sentence that follows and find the mistake. Remember a mistake can be a misspelled word or the wrong usage of a correctly spelled word. The misspelling or misused word will be included in a group of words. This group will be assigned a letter, and you'll need to mark this letter on the multiple choice answer grid.

Example

The boy	played happely	with his friends	on the field.	None
A	B	C	D	E

In the sentence above you can see that the word 'happely' is misspelled since it should be 'happily'. This word is in the group labelled B so you would mark B on your answer grid.

If you felt that there were no mistakes in the sentence you would mark E, which is under the word 'None'.

HELPFUL HINTS

- There are no grammatical mistakes in these questions, so don't worry about looking for these. See lessons 4, 8, 12, and 16 for questions where you have to identify grammatical errors.
- There are no words missing from the sentences – if the sentence does not seem to make sense then you'll need to read it again.
- Make sure you read each sentence fully and make sure that you understand what it means before looking for your answer. Some sentences will go over on to the next line so watch out for these.

LESSON 1 PART 1

My Time

My Score

Now look at the questions below. Work out where there are misspellings or correctly spelled but wrongly used words. Then mark your answer (the letter A, B, C or D) on the answer grid. If you think there are no mistakes in a particular question, mark option E. You have 10 minutes to complete the test. When you've finished, make a note of your time and score in the boxes above.

The river: part 1

1 Billy looked around uncertainly. He did not know wear he was, — None

A	B	C	D	E
Billy looked	around uncertainly.	He did not	know wear he was,	None

2 but he could here the sound of water from the river nearby. If he — None

A	B	C	D	E
but he could	here the sound	of water from the	river nearby. If he	None

3 could find it he knew they're would be fresh water to drink. He — None

A	B	C	D	E
could find it	he knew they're	would be fresh	water to drink. He	None

4 stumbled on through the jungle until he came to a clearing. He — None

A	B	C	D	E
stumbled on	through the jungle	until he came	to a clearing. He	None

5 saw the river now but he did not know ware his friends had gone. — None

A	B	C	D	E
saw the river	now but he did	not know ware	his friends had gone.	None

6 He could see there packs though, lying on the ground half open. — None

A	B	C	D	E
He could see there	packs though,	lying on the	ground half open.	None

7 'Their probably wandering about lost,' he muttered to himself. — None

A	B	C	D	E
'Their probably	wandering about	lost,'	he muttered to himself.	None

8 'But surely they will be able to find the way back to this river. It's — None

A	B	C	D	E
'But surely they	will be able to	find the way back	to this river. It's	None

9 huge.' He looked in a pack and saw his torch. 'That's not you're — None

A	B	C	D	E
huge.' He looked in	a pack and	saw his torch.	'That's not you're	None

10 torch Greg,' he murmured to himself, 'And anyway, your not using it now.' — None

A	B	C	D	E
torch Greg,' he	murmured to himself,	'And anyway, your not	using it now.'	None

LESSON 1 PART 1: ANSWER SHEET

Mark your answer by putting a horizontal line in one of the boxes as in the example below.

Example:

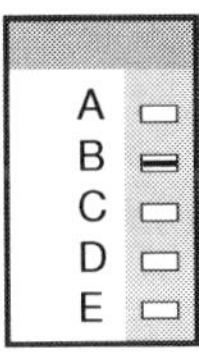

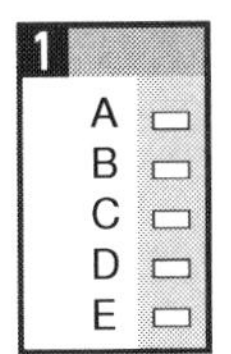

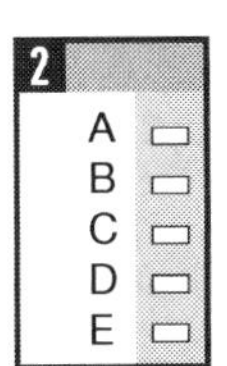

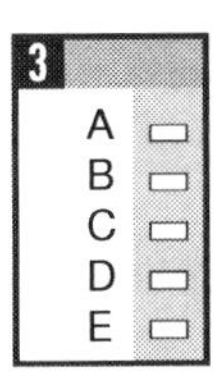

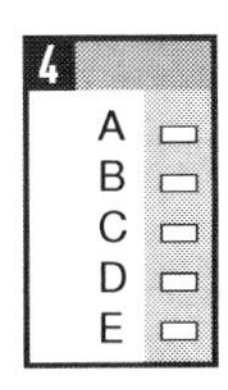

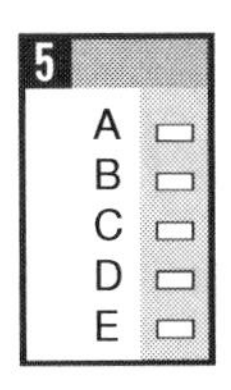

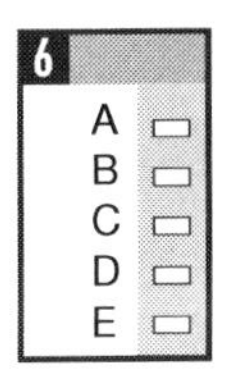

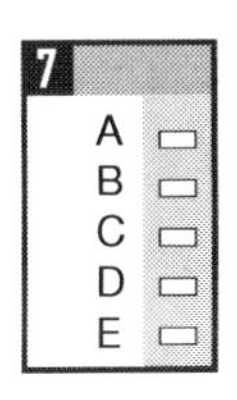

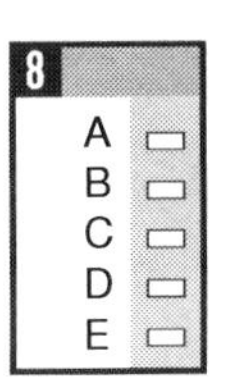

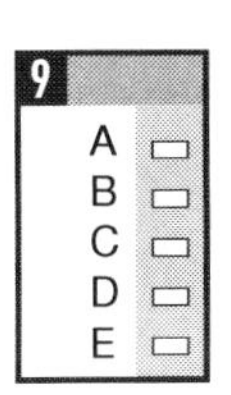

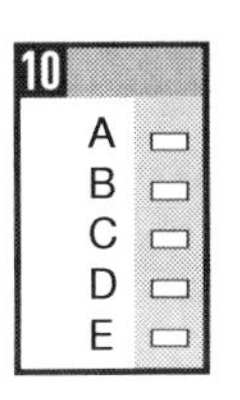

How Did You Do? Let's Find Out!

You can mark your answers to this lesson yourself. Here are the correct answers. For each answer I've written the letter that is the answer, the word that was used incorrectly or misspelled and the word that should have been used in brackets.

1	D	wear (where)
2	B	here (hear)
3	B	they're (there)
4	E	none
5	C	ware (where)
6	A	there (their)
7	A	their (they're)
8	E	none
9	D	you're (your)
10	C	your (you're)

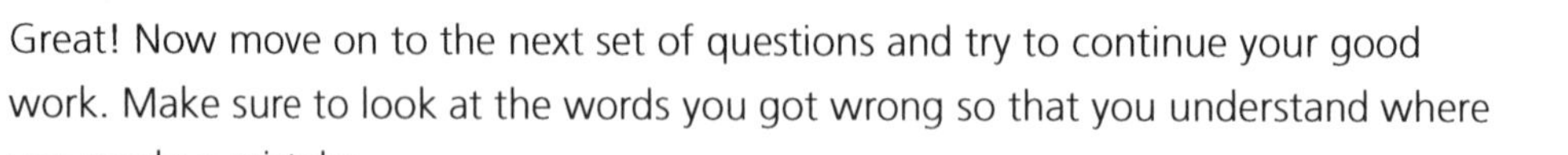

If you scored 8 or more out of 10

Great! Now move on to the next set of questions and try to continue your good work. Make sure to look at the words you got wrong so that you understand where you made a mistake.

If you scored 5 to 7 out of 10

Read this advice before moving on to the next set of questions.

- Look at the answers. You should know these words and how they should be used in a sentence. If you don't, go back to the spelling skills table on page 4 and use it to learn them.
- Did you notice that all of the questions had words that were used in the wrong context? Using a word in the wrong context counts as a spelling mistake and so you should have chosen the part of the sentence that included this word as your answer.
- Make sure you read the entire sentence and not just a line – that way you'll understand the context and be able to find out which word is being used incorrectly.

If you scored fewer than 5 out of 10

Read the suggestions that follow to help you improve your score.

- Do you understand what you have to do? If not, ask an adult to read the instructions and go through the example with you again. Then take another look at your answers and see if you can correct them.
- Do you understand how to mark your answers on the answer sheet? Sometimes students make mistakes on this because they haven't seen this kind of answer sheet before. Again, ask an adult to show you how to mark answers correctly on the answer sheet. Then do the questions once more.
- If you don't recognise some of the words or misspellings, make sure you practise your spelling and check the spelling skills table on page 4. Learn these words and make sure you understand the contexts in which they are used.
- Use the vocabulary builders on page 125 to help you learn and understand new words.
- Move on to the next set of 10 questions and see if you can score higher!

LESSON 1 PART 2

My Time

My Score

Now let's try some more. Work out where there are misspellings or wrongly used words. Then mark your answer (the letter A, B, C or D) on the answer grid. If you think there are no mistakes in a particular line, mark option E. You have 10 minutes to complete the test. Ask an adult to mark your answers for you and then you can fill in your time and score at the top of the page.

The river: part 2

	A	B	C	D	E
1	Billy looked	up at the sky.	It was becomeing dark	now and he	None
2	still hadn't	found his friends.	He felt quite	ancsious. 'It'll be	None
3	fine,' he whispered	to himself, but	he didn't	really beleive it.	None
4	Suddenley there	was a crack	in the trees	behind him. Billy	None
5	threw himself	to the floor	and cowerd, 'Is	anybody there?'	None
6	he stammered.	'No!' came the reply	in a loud,	echowing voice.	None
7	'We know where	you are,' the	voice sounded	again but this time	None
8	Billy reconised it.	'It's you lot!	You're hiding	somewhere!' he	None
9	shouted. Then	he saw a movment.	It was his	friends. 'I am glad	None
10	to see you,'	said Billy,	'I thought you were	lost in the forrest.'	None

LESSON 1 PART 2: ANSWER SHEET

Mark your answer by putting a horizontal line in one of the boxes as in the example below.

Example:

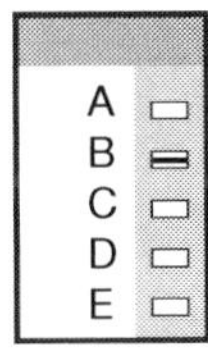

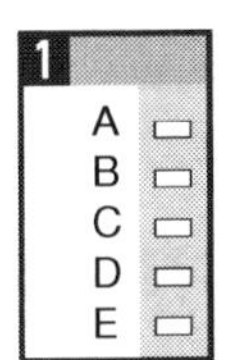

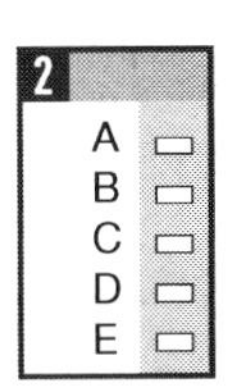

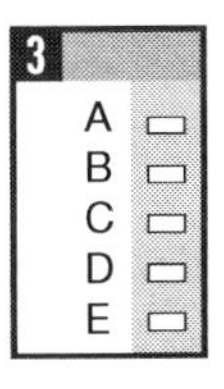

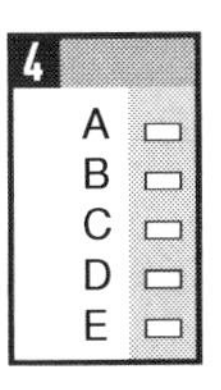

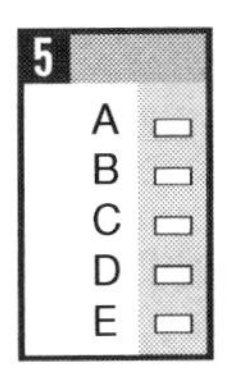

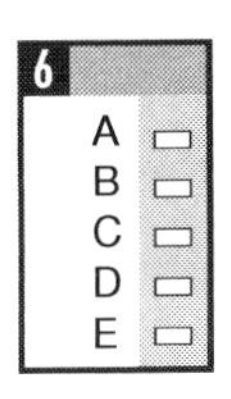

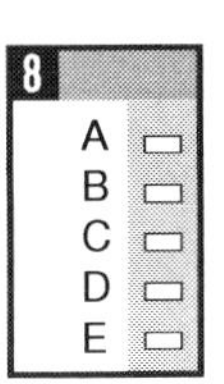

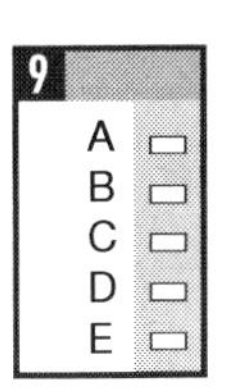

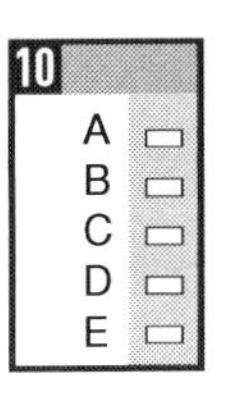

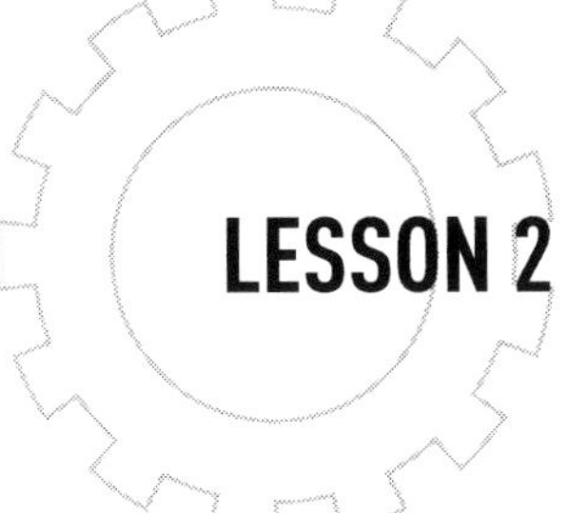

LESSON 2 Understanding Sentence Structure

In this exercise you'll need to choose one of the five boxed words to complete a sentence so that it makes sense. Once you've chosen your boxed word, mark the corresponding letter for that word (A, B, C, D or E) on your answer grid. Let's look at an example.

Example 1

The children [plaed] [plaid] [playd] [played] [plaied] on the swings.

A	B	C	D	E
plaed	plaid	playd	played	plaied

In the question above the correct answer is <u>played</u> so you need to mark <u>D</u> on the answer sheet. 'Played' is the correct past tense spelling of 'play' and is the only word that will complete the sentence so that it makes sense.

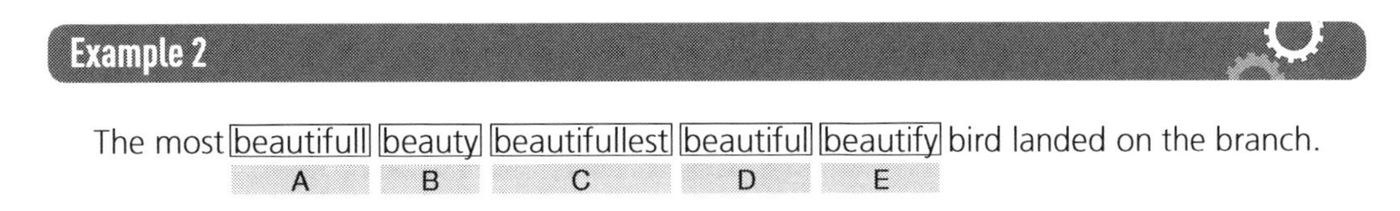

Example 2

The most [beautifull] [beauty] [beautifullest] [beautiful] [beautify] bird landed on the branch.

A	B	C	D	E
beautifull	beauty	beautifullest	beautiful	beautify

The correct answer is <u>beautiful</u> so you need to mark <u>D</u> on the multiple choice answer sheet.

LESSON 2 PART 1

My Time

My Score

Now look at the questions below. Work out which one of the words in the boxes will complete each sentence so that it makes sense. Then mark your answer (the letter A, B, C, D or E) on the answer grid. You will have 10 minutes to complete these.

The building site: part 1

1 The builders [was A] [why B] [where C] [were D] [we're E] working very hard.

2 [They A] [Thay B] [Thaye C] [Them D] [Theys E] were crashing and hammering all over the place.

3 Anybody walking past could [here A] [he're B] [her'e C] [hear D] [listen E] the noisy sounds.

4 Suddenly [their A] [there B] [they're C] [they D] [thare E] was a loud whistle and the noises stopped.

5 The builders began to [ate A] [eight B] [eat C] [aet D] [ete E] their lunch.

6 But they still had to [where A] [we're B] [were C] [ware D] [wear E] safety hats.

7 This was a rule to ensure [there A] [they B] [their C] [thay D] [thare E] safety.

8 All the builders [knowed A] [knew B] [new C] [knewe D] [knowing E] how important this was.

9 After lunch [had A] [is B] [will C] [were D] [are E] finished, work began again.

10 The [new A] [knew B] [nue C] [old D] [after E] building would soon be completed.

LESSON 2 PART 1: ANSWER SHEET

Mark your answer by putting a horizontal line in one of the boxes as in the examples below.

Example 1:

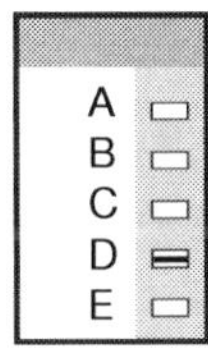

Example 2:

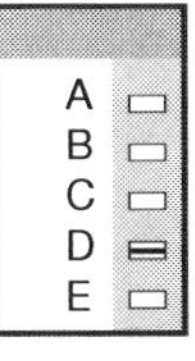

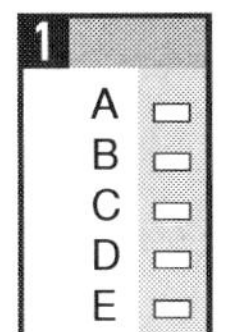

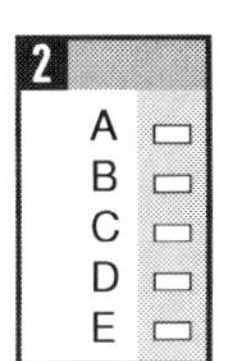

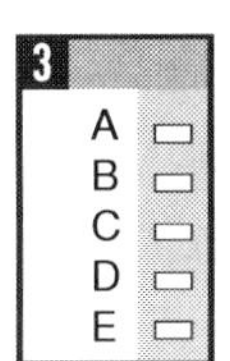

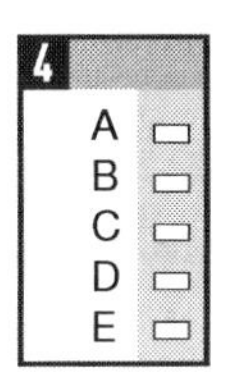

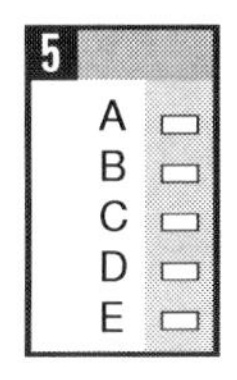

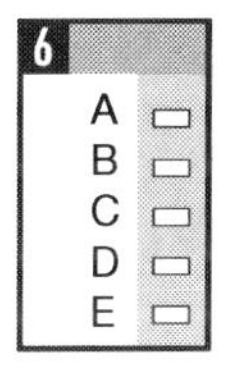

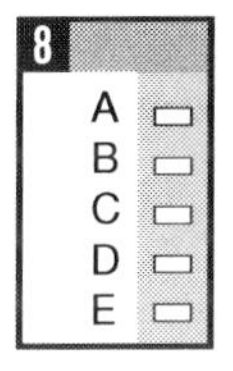

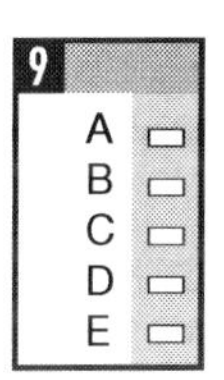

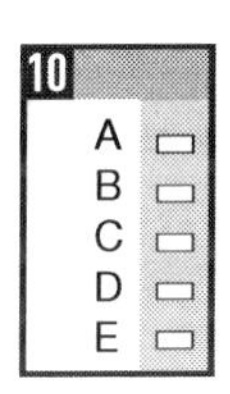

How Did You Do? Let's Find Out!

Here are the correct answers. You may mark your answers to these questions yourself. I've written the answer letter and the correct word so you can see where you went wrong.

1 D were

2 A They

3 D hear

4 B there

5 C eat

6 E wear

7 C their

8 B knew

9 A had

10 A new

If you scored 8 or more out of 10

This is a great score! Now move on to the next set of questions and see if you can continue your good work. Look at the words you got wrong before you start the next set though, to make sure you understand why you made mistakes.

If you scored 5 to 7 out of 10

Read the advice below before moving on to the next set of questions.

➪ Look at the answers. You should know all of these words and how they should be used in a sentence. If you don't, go back and look at the spelling skills table on page 4 and use it to learn the words and how they should be used. If they aren't in the spelling table, use the vocabulary builder on page 125. Write the words down and look them up in a dictionary so you'll know them in future.

If you scored fewer than 5 out of 10

Read the suggestions that follow to find out how you can get a better score.

➪ Do you understand what you have to do? If not, ask an adult to read the instructions and go through the example with you again. Then take another look at your answers and see if you can correct them.

➪ Do you understand how to mark your answers on the answer sheet? Again ask an adult to show you how to mark answers correctly. Then do the questions once more.

➪ Use the vocabulary builders on page 125 to help you with new words. Make sure you know how these words should be used in a sentence.

LESSON 2 PART 2

My Time

My Score

Now look at the questions below. Work out which one of the five boxed words will complete each sentence so that it makes sense. Then mark your answer (the letter A, B, C, D or E) on the answer grid. You will have 10 minutes to complete these. Ask an adult to mark these for you and then you can fill in your time and score at the top of the page.

The building site: part 2

1 It [was A] [wos B] [where C] [were D] [waz E] early morning on the building site.

2 The foreman arrived and told them [wat A] [what B] [wait C] [wot D] [waht E] to do.

3 The builders listened and got [strate A] [straight B] [strait C] [strayt D] [straite E] to work.

4 On this day [thay A] [theye B] [their C] [there D] [they E] were starting to build a tower.

5 They [wood A] [wud B] [would C] [wered D] [word E] mark out the foundations first.

6 Then the concrete [were A] [had B] [will C] [are D] [shall E] to be poured into the hole.

7 Next the builders needed to [wate A] [wait B] [weight C] [waite D] [what E] for it to set.

8 Then they began [to A] [two B] [too C] [tow D] [toe E] mark out the walls.

9 They [carried A] [carryed B] [card C] [carryied D] [carred E] many bricks to the site.

10 But they still had [soo A] [soe B] [sew C] [so D] [soh E] much to do before it would be finished!

LESSON 2 PART 2: ANSWER SHEET

Mark your answer by putting a horizontal line in one of the boxes as in the examples below.

Example 1:

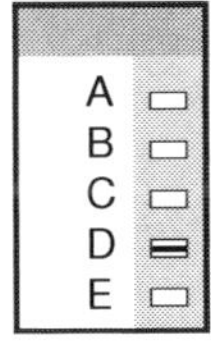

Example 2:

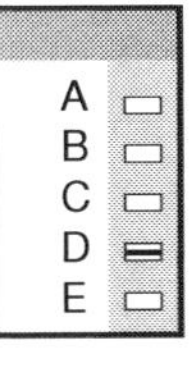

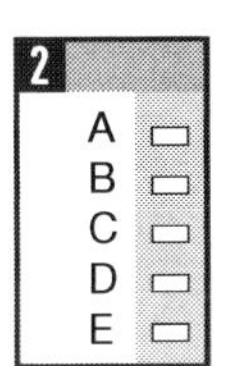

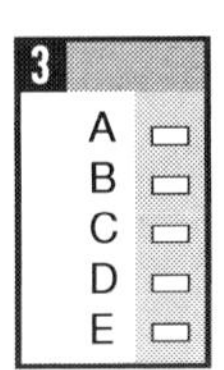

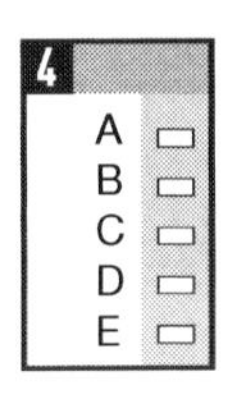

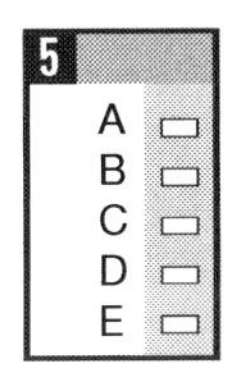

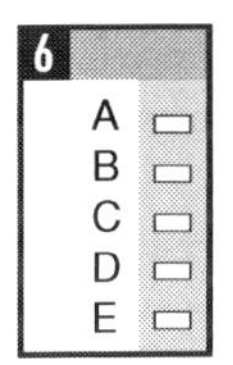

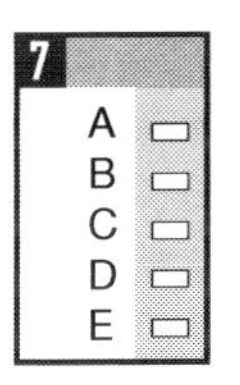

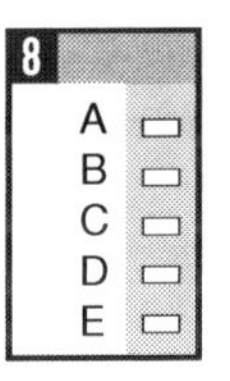

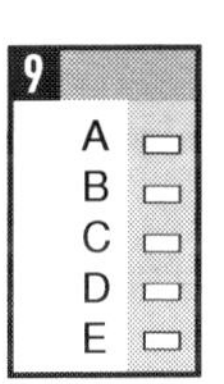

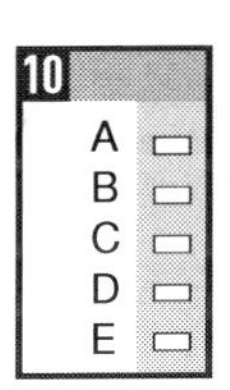

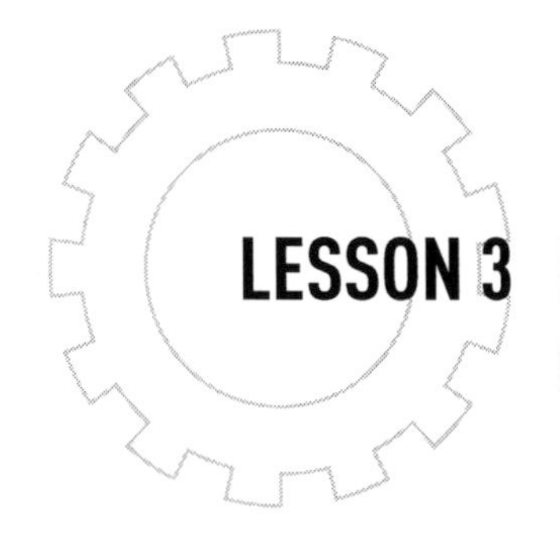

LESSON 3 Improving Your Punctuation Skills: Capital Letters

In this exercise you'll need to spot the punctuation errors in each line of text. To do this correctly you'll need to have a good understanding of the basic rules of punctuation and when they each apply.

When you're doing the exercise, you'll notice that each sentence is divided into four parts and each part has a letter under it (A, B, C or D). You'll need to see which part of the sentence has a punctuation mistake and put a mark against the corresponding letter on the answer sheet. If there is no mistake in the sentence, choose option E.

Let's begin by looking at the use of capital letters and full stops.

Capital letters

1 Capital letters are used to begin a new sentence.

Example 1

the forest seemed dark and spooky.

The sentence above should be written as:

<u>T</u>he forest seemed dark and spooky.

This sentence starts with 'the' so 'the' should have a capital T, as underlined above.

---

2 A capital letter is used for 'i' when you are talking about yourself.

Example 2

Can i go to the shops with you?

The sentence above should be written as:

Can <u>I</u> go to the shops with you?

Whenever 'i' is used to talk about oneself, it should be a capital.

HELPFUL HINTS

- A full stop is used at the end of a complete statement. Any sentence that follows a full stop must start with a capital letter.
- If you see a sentence which appears to have a word beginning with a capital in the middle of it, check it again. The word may be a proper noun but if it isn't, a full stop may be missing.

3 Whenever you use a proper noun, it should start with a capital letter. If you're not sure what a proper noun is, read the next section to find out.

What is a proper noun?

Proper nouns are the names that we give to objects to identify them. For example, names of people, countries, cities, mountains, rivers, products, days of the week, months of the year, and religious festivals are all proper nouns.

Remember that proper nouns always begin with a capital letter.

Complete the table below before you move on to the questions; it will help you make sure you understand proper nouns.

Category	My example	Your example 1	Your example 2	Your example 3
people	Shakespeare			
countries	France			
cities	Paris			
mountains	Andes			
rivers	Orinoco			
products	Mercedes			
days	Monday			
months	April			
planets	Jupiter			
festivals	Christmas			
titles	Mr (Mister)			

To help you remember what a noun is, just keep in mind a noun is a person, a place or an object (a thing!).

LESSON 3 PART 1

My Time

My Score

Now look at the questions below. Work out where capital letters and full stops have been left out. Then mark your answer (the letter A, B, C or D) on the answer grid. If you think there are no mistakes in a particular question, mark option E on the answer grid. You have 10 minutes to complete the test.

The surgery: part 1

	A	B	C	D	E
1	the old man	tottered into the	surgery and looked	for a spare seat.	None
2	There weren't	any but a young	lady stood up	so he could have	None
3	hers The	old man was	very grateful and	thanked her as he	None
4	painfully sat	down.'Who are	you here to see?'	he asked.	None
5	'Doctor south,'	she replied.	'Is your back	causing you pain?'	None
6	'It's terrible,'	he said. 'I	hope i can see	Doctor Blewitt. He is very	None
7	good when it comes	to sorting out	my back. he	always takes the	None
8	time to find out	exactly where	the problem is.	is Doctor South nice?'	None
9	'Extremely nice,'	said the lady.	'She has been	my doctor all my	None
10	life. We're very	lucky to have	such lovely people	to help us'	None

LESSON 3 PART 1: ANSWER SHEET

Mark your answer by putting a horizontal line in one of the boxes for each answer below.

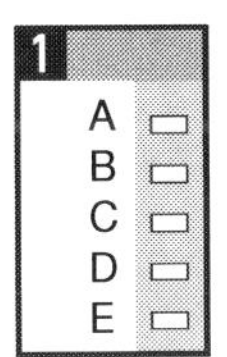

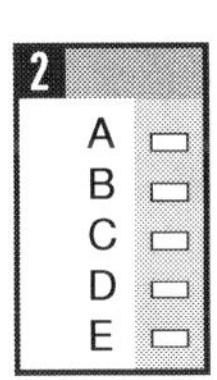

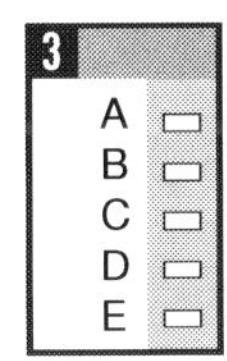

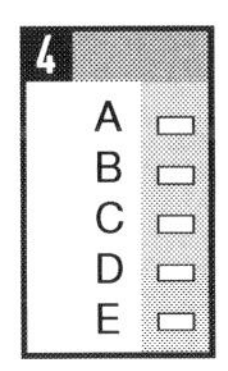

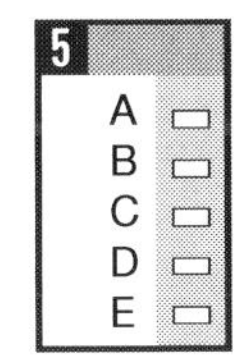

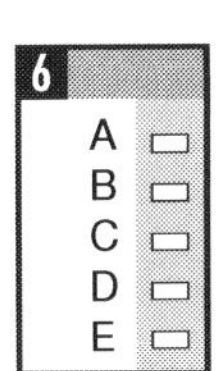

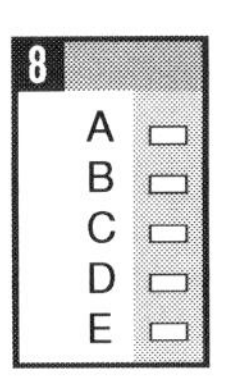

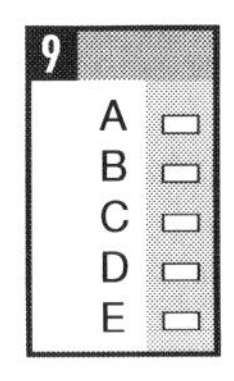

How Did You Do? Let's Find Out!

Here are the correct answers. You may mark your answers to these questions yourself. The correct punctuation or capital letters are written next to the answer letter so that you can see what the answer should be.

1 A The

2 E none

3 A hers.

4 B 'Who

5 A South

6 C I

7 C He

8 D Is

9 E none

10 D us.'

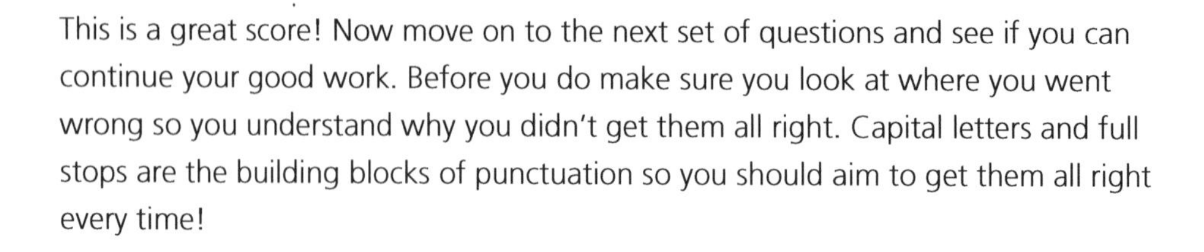

If you scored 9 or more out of 10

This is a great score! Now move on to the next set of questions and see if you can continue your good work. Before you do make sure you look at where you went wrong so you understand why you didn't get them all right. Capital letters and full stops are the building blocks of punctuation so you should aim to get them all right every time!

If you scored 7 or 8 out of 10

Take a look at the following advice before moving on to the next set of questions.

➪ Make sure that you read the complete sentences and look for the clues. If a sentence seems to have a capital letter in the middle, either that word is a proper noun or it should be the start of a new sentence, and there should be a full stop before it.

➪ Look at beginning of each sentence to check first letter of first word has a capital letter.

If you scored 6 or fewer out of 10

Fewer than 6 is quite a low score. Read the suggestions that follow so you can improve for next time.

➪ If you don't understand the question, ask an adult to read the instructions and go through the example with you again. Then take another look at your answers and see if you can correct them.

➪ Make sure you understand exactly where full stops and capital letters should be used. You really must be strong on these. Look at examples on pages 20–21 again.

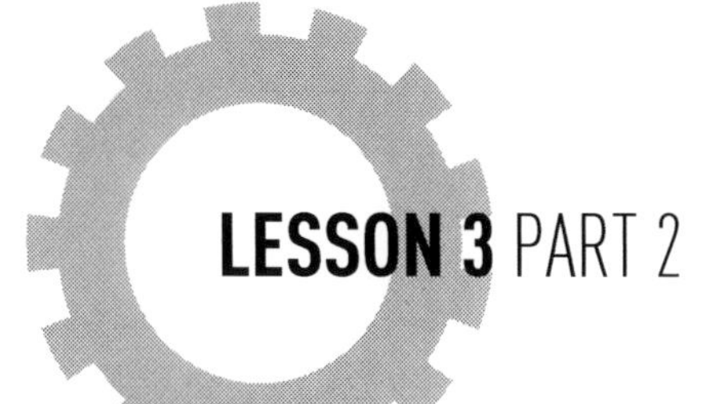

LESSON 3 PART 2

My Time

My Score

Now look at the questions below. Work out where capital letters and full stops have been left out and mark your answer (the letter A, B, C or D) on the answer grid. If you think there are no mistakes in a particular line then mark option E on the answer grid. You will have 10 minutes to complete these. Ask an adult to mark these for you. Then write your time and score in the boxes at the top.

The surgery: part 2

No.	A	B	C	D	None (E)
1	The old man	introduced himself	as Mr cork	He asked the kind	None
2	lady what	her name was and	she replied that	it was Mrs trott.	None
3	then there was	the sound of a	buzzer and a loud	voice said, 'Mrs	None
4	Trott, Doctor blewitt	will see you	now in room	three.' Mrs Trott	None
5	stood up slowly	and smiled	again at mr Cork.	'I hope you get	None
6	seen soon,' she	mouthed as she	headed towards	room three. he	None
7	waved back at her,	'Good luck	and I hope	everything is alright,' he	None
8	answered. then	another loud voice	called, 'Mr Cork,	Doctor South	None
9	will see you now	in room one.'	Mr Cork rose	painfully but was	None
10	relieved that	he would be	seeing the	doctor so soon	None

LESSON 3 PART 2: ANSWER SHEET

Mark your answer by putting a horizontal line in one of the boxes for each answer below.

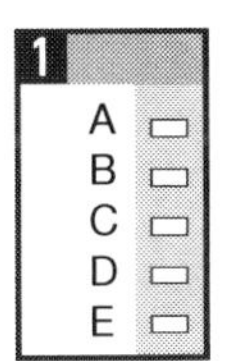

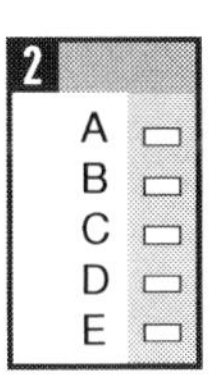

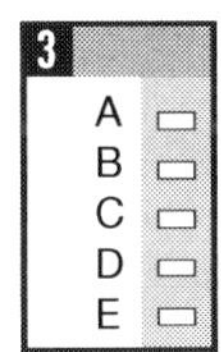

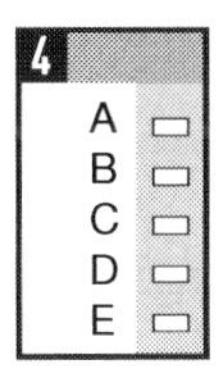

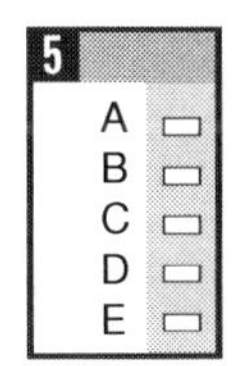

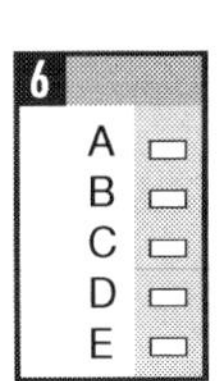

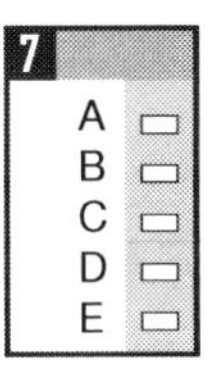

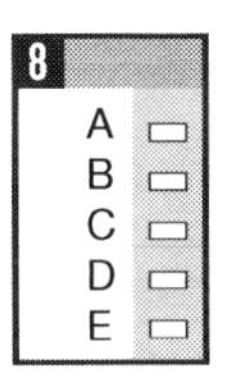

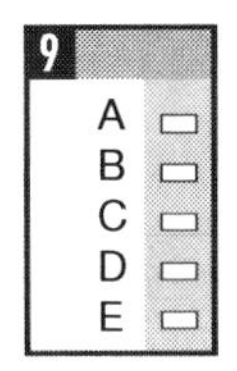

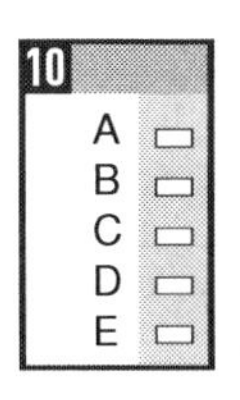

LESSON 4 Practising Comprehension and Grammar

In this exercise you're asked to read a passage of text and then answer some questions about it. This lesson is a bit different to the ones you've already worked on as it's in three sections. This is because this kind of exercise tests two types of skill at the same time: comprehension and grammar.

The first section of the lesson talks you through what to look out for in terms of comprehension and the second helps you improve your grammar. The third section is where you'll find the practice questions.

So let's get started!

A Improving Your Comprehension: Closed Questions

To do well at comprehension questions it's important that you recognise the style of question you are being asked. We'll begin by looking at closed questions.

Typically these questions require you to find a definite answer from the passage meaning you have to find a piece of detail from the text. You aren't expected to give an explanation or your own opinion. Often, such questions begin with:

- ➪ 'Who was/were…'
- ➪ 'What was/were…'
- ➪ 'When was/were…'

Let's look at an example.

Example

Arnold headed towards the bookcase. It was dusty and covered in cobwebs.

1 What did Arnold head towards?

A the cobwebs
B the dust
C the covers
D the bookcase
E his house

The answer to the question above is D – the bookcase. Although it is described as being covered with dust and cobwebs, Arnold was heading for the bookcase and not what it was covered with. That's why D is the correct answer.

Questions for comprehension skills follow the next part of this lesson, which is on grammar skills.

B Improving Your Grammar: Adjectives

Here we'll tackle some of the more common types of grammar problem, which you need to know really well. Let's start by looking at adjectives.

Adjectives are words we use to describe or give us more information about a noun.

Adjectives usually come directly before (and very occasionally) after a noun. They can also be used with the verb 'to be' (and all of its tenses) to describe a noun in a sentence. Let's look at some examples to show each of these.

Example 1

In the field, there stood an old tree.

In the example above, the word old is an adjective as it describes the tree. It tells us more information about the tree – that it is old.

Example 2

In the field there was a tree, old but still standing.

In the example above, the adjective is still the word old but this time it comes after the noun – the word tree.

Example 3

The tree standing in the field was old.

In the example above, yet again the adjective is the word old but this time it follows the past tense of the verb to be (was is the past tense of the verb 'to be').

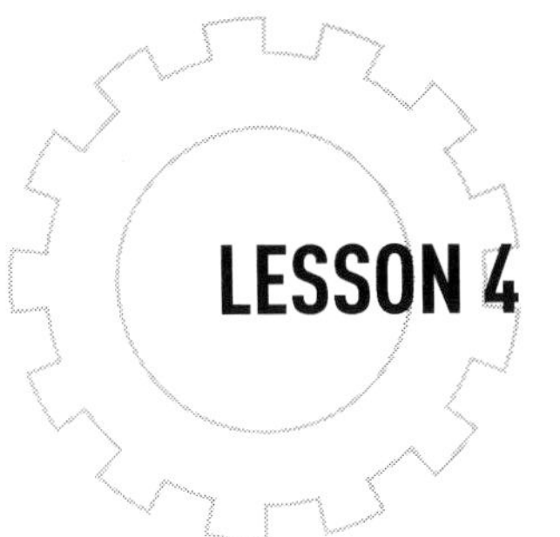

LESSON 4 Practice Questions

My Time

My Score

Read the passage below carefully and answer the questions that follow. They may be comprehension or grammar questions as we saw in lesson 4 A and B. When you think you've worked out the correct answer, mark your answer on the corresponding answer grid on page 33. Ask an adult to mark your answers for you. You should be able to complete these in about 10 minutes. This time includes the time you have to read the passage.

The beggar

In the extract that follows, Sergeant Bilius discovers a beggar in the palace grounds, who seems to have a special past.

1 His skin was gnarled and cracked from many years spent in the glare of hostile sunlight. Yet his grip seemed deceptively strong for one who seemed so ancient and weak. He steadfastly maintained his grasp around the wooden shaft, and though his nails, which were worn and uneven like old weathered stone, looked brittle to the eye, they too appeared to own some hidden strength.

2 And on this smoke-filled autumnal day, with the sun's rays weakening and diving behind the damp woods, Sergeant Bilius looked down in pity at the beggar who kneeled before his horse and yet would not relinquish his grip on the shovel handle. This poor man who protected his precious property without regard for his own safety, was not the normal type.

3 Just then, he glanced at the man's rough joints and noticed a strange, if faded, mark. The tattoo was that of the royal household, but surely that was not possible, was it?

4 Sergeant Bilius allowed the beggar to pull the shovel away. Without a word, he turned his horse and headed for the royal stables – his captain had to be notified of this at once!

1 How is the beggar's skin described by the author? (paragraph 1)

A smooth and soft
B old and grey
C weathered and brittle
D gnarled and cracked
E strong and clever

2 In the phrase 'the wooden shaft...' 'wooden' is an example of a: (paragraph 1)

A noun
B adjective
C adverb
D verb
E conjunction

3 What were the beggar's nails like? (paragraph 1)

A smooth and perfect
B smooth and clean
C worn but polished
D worn and uneven
E strong and brittle

4 What part of speech is 'stone'? (paragraph 1)

A verb
B noun
C adjective
D adverb
E pronoun

5 What was the beggar doing in front of Sergeant Bilius's horse? (paragraph 2)

A walking
B crawling
C standing
D staggering
E kneeling

6 In the phrase 'the damp woods...' 'damp' is an example of a: (paragraph 2)

A preposition
B pronoun
C verb
D adverb
E adjective

7 In the phrase 'rough joints...', what part of speech is 'rough'? (paragraph 3)

A verb
B adjective
C proper noun
D adverb
E noun

8 What did the beggar have on his skin? (paragraph 3)

A mud
B ointment
C a bandage
D a cut
E a tattoo

9 What part of speech is 'Bilius'? (paragraph 4)

A proper noun
B common noun
C abstract noun
D concrete noun
E pronoun

10 Who did Sergeant Bilius go to tell about what he had found? (paragraph 4)

A his king
B his queen
C his captain
D his sergeant
E his soldiers

LESSON 4 PART 3: ANSWER SHEET

Mark your answer by putting a horizontal line in one of the boxes as in the example below.

Example:

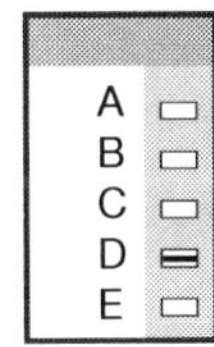

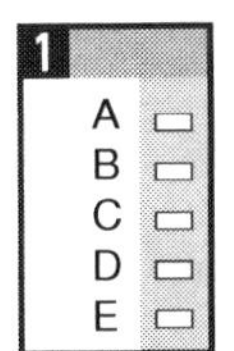
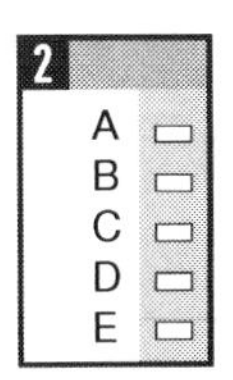
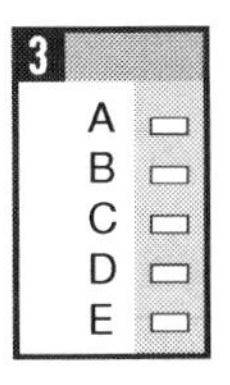
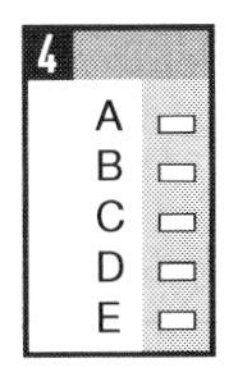
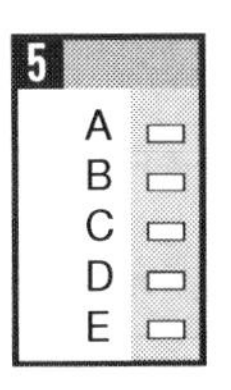

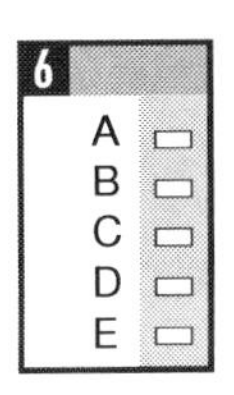
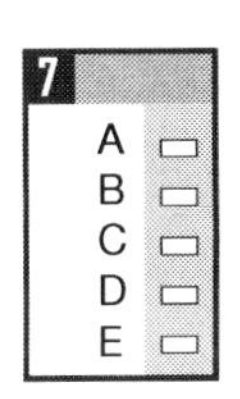
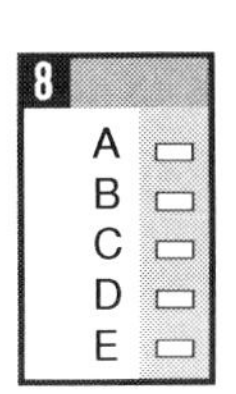

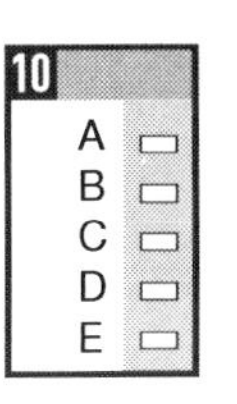

SECTION 2

LESSON 5 Improving Your Spelling Skills

In this exercise you'll be looking for words that are spelled incorrectly and for words that are misused, as you did in lesson 1. Let's look at some more examples.

Word	Meaning	Clue
whose	Who does this belong to? 'Whose pencil is this?'	
who's	'Who is' becomes 'Who's' – 'Who's coming to the shop with me?'	Remember that an apostrophe tells us two words have been combined.
were	Past tense of 'are' – 'They were travelling yesterday.'	
we're	'We are' becomes 'We're'. 'We're going on holiday tomorrow.'	Remember that an apostrophe tells us two words have been combined.
weir	Pronounced like 'hear' but with 'w' at the beginning. It also sounds like 'we're'. A weir is a dam across a river.	Think of the word 'weird' and remove the 'd' from the end to help remember pronounciation.
are	The present tense of the verb 'to be' – 'We are very happy.'	Learn it – you should know all the main parts of the verb 'to be'.
our	This word should be pronounced like 'hour' – it means it belongs to us.	Think of 'hour' but remove the 'h'.
hour	A unit of time – there are 60 minutes in an hour.	
aloud	A noise made out loud so it can be heard.	Think of the word 'loud' then add an 'a' on the front.
allowed	You have permission – 'You're allowed to go in there.'	Check to see if the word means a noise – if it does, use 'aloud' (see above); if not, use this one.

Make sure you have learned the spellings above before you try the practice questions.

Now here's an example question. Read the sentence that follows and find the mistakes. A mistake can be a misspelled word or the wrong usage of a correctly spelled word. The mistake is included in a group of words which is assigned a letter, and it's this letter that you'll need to mark on the answer sheet.

Example

The girl sat in the garden and red her book. None

The girl	sat in	the garden and	red her book.	None
A	B	C	D	E

In the sentence above you can see that the word 'red' is used incorrectly as it should be 'read'. This word is in the group labelled C so you should mark C on your answer grid.

If you felt that there were no mistakes in the sentence you would mark E, which is under the word 'None'.

HELPFUL HINTS

- There are no grammatical mistakes in these questions.
- There are no words missing in these questions.
- Make sure that you read the whole sentence. Sometimes they will be split over two lines, so make sure you watch out for these.
- Remember – a word that is spelled correctly but used in the wrong context also counts as a spelling mistake.

LESSON 5 PART 1

My Time

My Score

Now look at the questions below. Work out where there are misspellings or correctly spelled but wrongly used words. Then mark your answer (the letter A, B, C or D) on the answer grid. If you think there are no mistakes in a particular question, mark option E. You have 10 minutes to complete the test.

The funfair: part 1

	A	B	C	D	None E
1	Max and Gil	we're excited	because the funfair	had come to town.	E
2	Their parents	had aloud them	to go alone for	the first time. When	E
3	the our came	for them to leave,	they waved	goodbye and set off.	E
4	'Do you know	where to go Gil?'	asked Max	excitedly.	E
5	'Of course,'	replied Gil, 'were	going to follow	the bright lights.'	E
6	'What our we going	to try first when	we get there?'	asked Max.	E
7	'I think we should	ride on the	ghost train,'	grinned Gil.	E
8	'Ooh yes – weir	is it – can you	see it yet?' Max	asked happily.	E
9	'There it is!'	shouted Gil.	'Whose going to	get on first?'	E
10	'Not me!' Max	shouted allowed.	'You know I get	really scared!'	E

LESSON 5 PART 1: ANSWER SHEET

Mark your answer by putting a horizontal line in one of the boxes as in the example below.

Example:

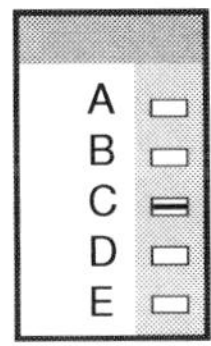

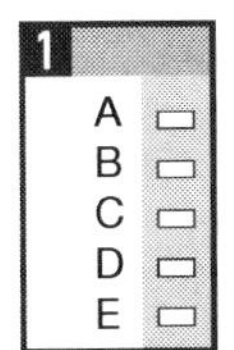

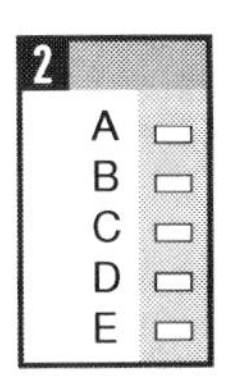

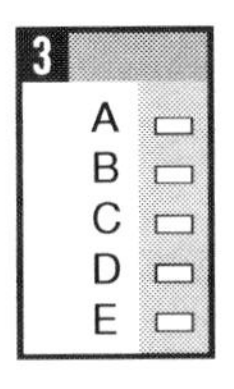

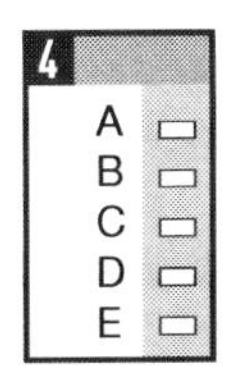

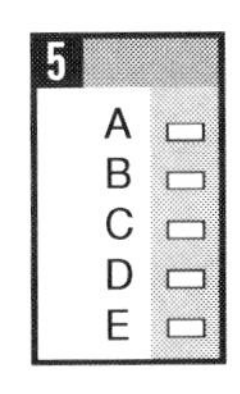

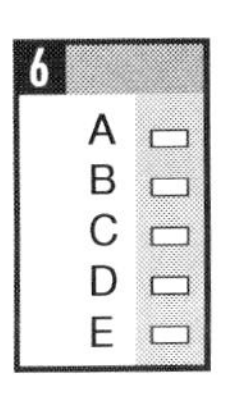

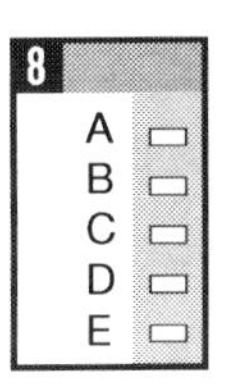

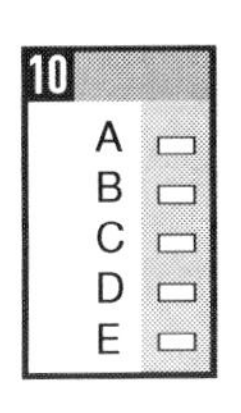

How Did You Do? Let's Find Out!

Here are the correct answers. You may mark your answers to these questions yourself. I've written the answer letter, the misused or misspelled word and the correct word (in brackets) so you can understand each answer.

1 B we're (were)

2 B aloud (allowed)

3 A our (hour)

4 E none

5 B were (we're)

6 A our (are)

7 E none

8 A weir (where)

9 C Whose (Who's)

10 B allowed (aloud)

If you scored 8 or more out of 10

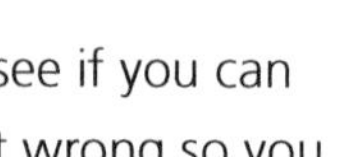

This is a great score! Now move on to the next set of questions and see if you can continue your good work. Make sure you check any answers you got wrong so you can get them right next time.

If you scored 5 to 7 out of 10 

➪ Look at the correct answers. You should know all of the words and how they should be used. If you don't, go back and look at the spelling skills tables on pages 4 and 34 to make sure you know them all.

➪ Can you see that all of the questions had words that were used in the wrong context? This is the mistake you need to identify and mark as your answer.

➪ Make sure you read the entire sentence and not just one line – that way you'll be better able to spot which word is being used incorrectly.

If you scored fewer than 5 out of 10 

Read the suggestions that follow before moving on to the next set of questions, to make sure you improve your score.

➪ Do you understand what you have to do? If not, ask an adult to read the instructions and go through the example with you again. Then take another look at your answers and see if you can correct them.

➪ Do you understand how to mark your answers on the answer sheet? Check you know how to fill in the answer sheet and take care. You don't want to know the answer but fill in the wrong answer.

➪ If you didn't recognise some of the words, make sure you understand the differences between the words and when you should use each one. Check the spelling skills tables on pages 4 and 34 to help you.

➪ Use the vocabulary builders on page 125 to help you with new words.

LESSON 5 PART 2

My Time	My Score

Now let's try some more. Work out where there are misspelled or wrongly used words and mark your answer (the letter A, B, C or D) on the answer grid. If you think there are no mistakes in a particular line then mark option E on the answer grid. You have 10 minutes to complete these. Ask an adult to mark these for you. Then write your time and score in the box at the top.

The funfair: part 2

	A	B	C	D	E
1	'Alright,' said Gil,	'I'll have	the first go,	then it will be your	None
2	tern.' Max	nodded his agreement	but he still	looked very nervous.	None
3	As the cart	came round, Gil	hoped inside and	put the safety bar	None
4	down. With a	huge grin and	a wave Gil	set of into the	None
5	darkness. It wasn't	long before he	emereged from the	other end	None
6	with a great	big smile on his	face. He leappt	out then shouted	None
7	aloud what	wonderfull fun it	had been. Max	walked slowly	None
8	towards the next	cart. 'You're not	frightened are you?'	asked Gil	None
9	mischievously. Max	gulped, 'Not at	all,' he	replyed, 'Who's	None
10	scarred of a	ghost train anyway?	It's only a	ride at the fair.'	None

LESSON 5 PART 2: ANSWER SHEET

Mark your answer by putting a horizontal line in one of the boxes as in the example below.

Example:

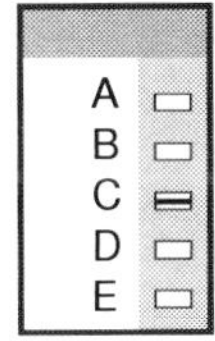

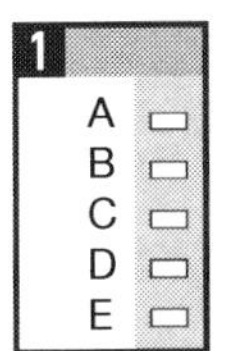
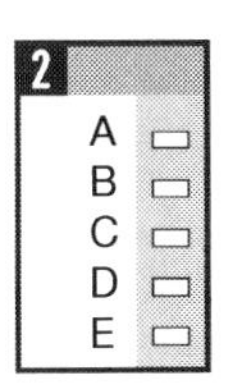
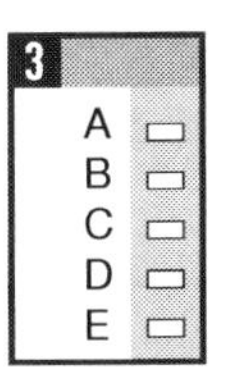
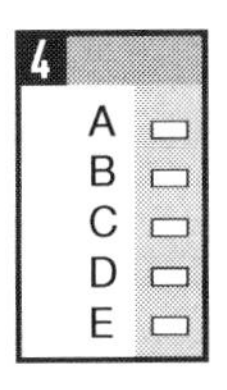
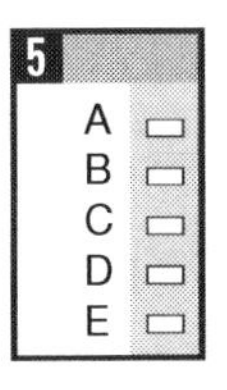

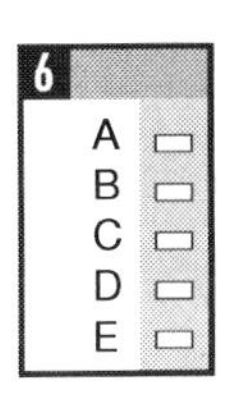
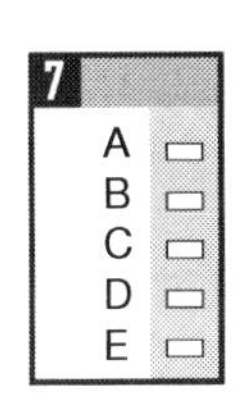
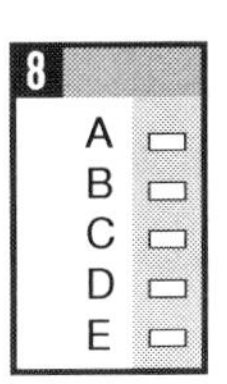
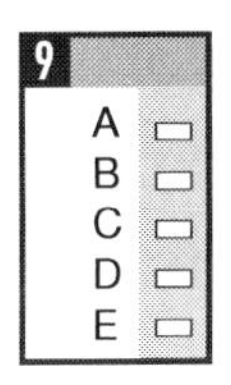
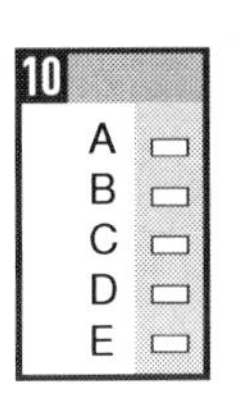

LESSON 6 Understanding Sentence Structure

In this exercise you'll be asked the same kind of question that you've already answered in lesson 2. Remember, you'll need to choose one of five words which will complete the sentence so that it makes sense. Let's take a look at some examples.

Example 1

The children [chatered | chattrd | chatterd | chattered | chattering] during their break.

A	B	C	D	E
chatered	chattrd	chatterd	chattered	chattering

In the question above the correct answer is chattered so you would mark D on the answer sheet.

Example 2

The helicopter's rotors [were | weird | warred | whired | whirred] round and round.

A	B	C	D	E
were	weird	warred	whired	whirred

The answer is whirred so you would mark E on the multiple choice answer sheet.

HELPFUL HINT

Read the sentence using each word, one at a time, and then eliminate any answers which simply don't make sense when you read the sentence as a whole. For example, the words 'were', 'weird' and 'warred' all sound wrong so ignore these. This allows you to concentrate on the two remaining possible answers 'whired' and 'whirred'. This method will help you focus on spotting the words which make sense but are perhaps spelled incorrectly.

LESSON 6 PART 1

My Time

My Score

Now look at the questions below. Work out which one of the words in the boxes will complete each sentence in the best way. Then mark your answer (the letter A, B, C, D or E) on the answer grid. You will have 10 minutes to complete these.

The strange travellers: part 1

1 The travellers [was | who | weir | were | we're] tired after their long journey.
A B C D E

2 They had been on the road for many an [our | are | ower | hour | aire].
A B C D E

3 Nobody knew [wear | weir | where | ware | were] they came from,
A B C D E

4 or how far they [had | was | are | were | is] travelled, for they spoke
A B C D E

5 strangely and [war | wore | wear | weared | wared] curious clothes.
A B C D E

6 They set up camp and fed [there | their | they're | these | this] animals.
A B C D E

7 The animals [whose | whos | who's | who'se | hoos] backs were
A B C D E

8 humped, did not need to [eet | eight | ate | eat | aet] very much food.
A B C D E

9 The travellers did not seem [to | two | too | toe | tow] be concerned
A B C D E

10 by this and then [build | built | builded | billed | bilt] a camp fire.
A B C D E

LESSON 6 PART 1: ANSWER SHEET

Mark your answer by putting a horizontal line in one of the boxes as in the examples below.

Example 1:

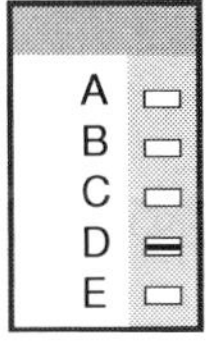

Example 2:

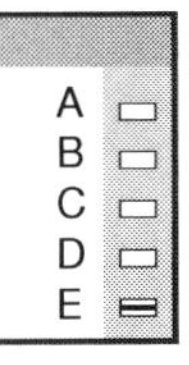

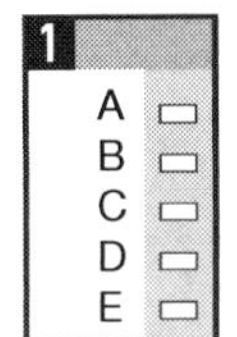

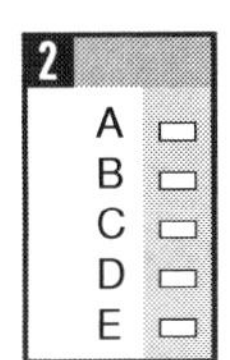

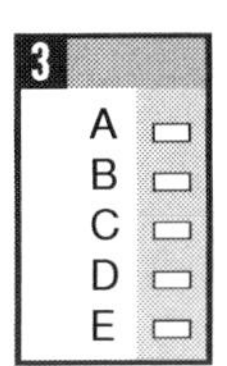

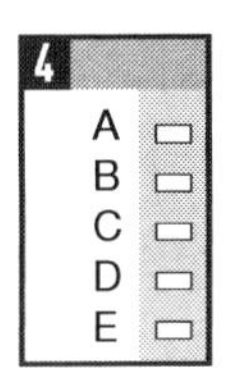

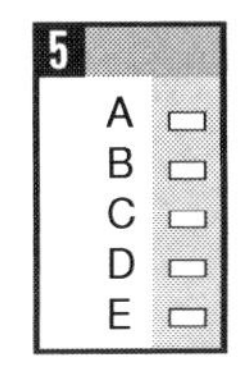

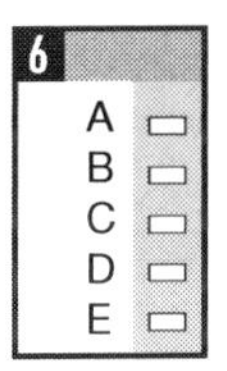

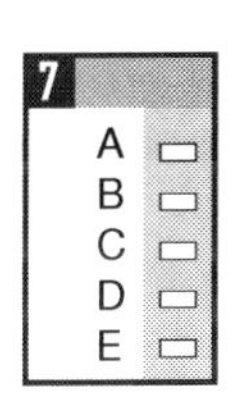

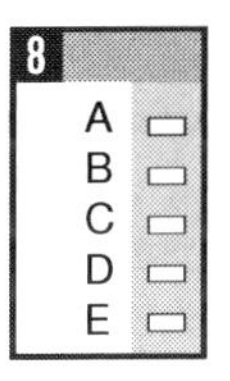

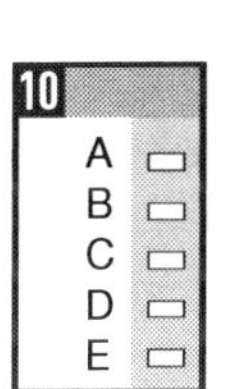

How Did You Do? Let's Find Out!

Here are the correct answers. You may mark your answers to these questions yourself. I have given you the correct letter and word so you can fully understand the answer.

1	D	were
2	D	hour
3	C	where
4	A	had
5	B	wore
6	B	their
7	A	whose
8	D	eat
9	A	to
10	B	built

If you scored 8 or more out of 10

Well done! Look at the words you got wrong so you can see where you made mistakes. Then move on to the next set of questions and see if you can continue your good work.

If you scored 5 to 7 out of 10

Look at the answers. You should know all of these words and understand when they should be used. If you don't, go back and look at the spelling skills tables on pages 4 and 34. If some of the words aren't in the spelling table, use the vocabulary builders on page 125 to write down the words and look them up in a dictionary so you'll know them in future.

If you scored fewer than 5 out of 10

Read the suggestions that follow to help you improve before moving on to the next set of questions.

➪ Do you understand how to mark your answers on the answer sheet? Again ask an adult to show you how to mark answers correctly, then do the questions once more.

➪ Use the vocabulary builders on page 125 to help you learn new words.

LESSON 6 PART 2

My Time

My Score

Now look at the questions below. Work out which one of the five boxed words will complete each sentence so that it makes sense. Then mark your answer (the letter A, B, C, D or E) on the answer grid. You have 10 minutes to complete the test. Ask an adult to mark these for you. Then write your time and score in the box at the top.

The strange travellers: part 2

1 [Wen A] [When B] [Wane C] [Whene D] [Whain E] the fire was burning, the travellers

2 laid blankets on the ground and [sits A] [sats B] [sitted C] [sat D] [sitting E] around it.

3 Thenther e [wear A] [weir B] [where C] [we're D] [were E] lovely smells as they began

4 toc ook [there A] [they're B] [thare C] [their D] [them E] evening meal. Meat and

5 vegetabless izzled [while A] [wile B] [whyle C] [whyall D] [whil E] drinks of water

6 and fruit juice were [past A] [parsed B] [passed C] [parst D] [parssed E] around.

7 Later on, when everyone [is A] [are B] [were C] [will D] [had E] finished eating, music

8 [c ud A] [cooed B] [culd C] [could D] [cold E] be heard. It was a strange sound, more like

9 awei rd [wailing A] [whaling B] [waling C] [weeling D] [wayling E]. And it all drifted

10 across the oasis [two A] [too B] [tow C] [to D] [tou E] the other camps.

LESSON 6 PART 2: ANSWER SHEET

Mark your answer by putting a horizontal line in one of the boxes as in the examples below.

Example 1:

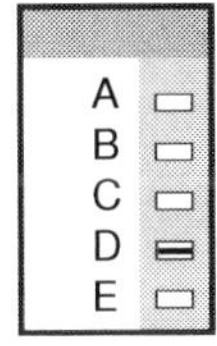

Example 2:

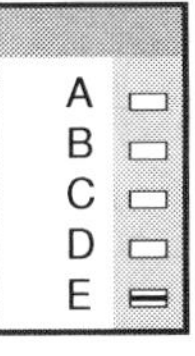

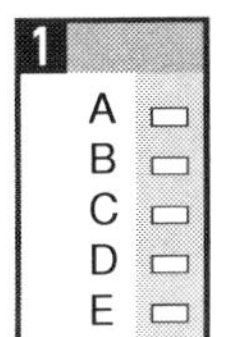
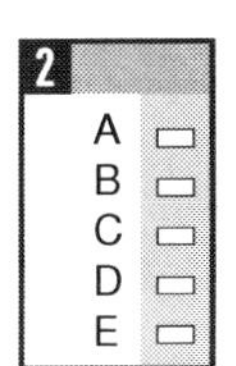
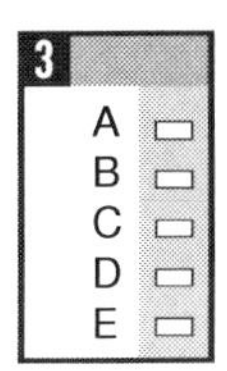
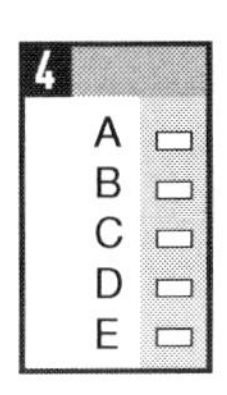
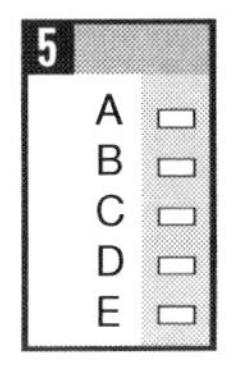

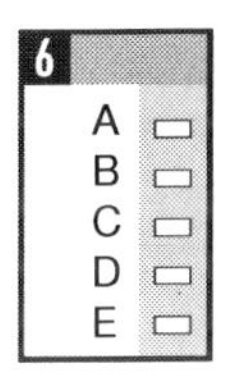
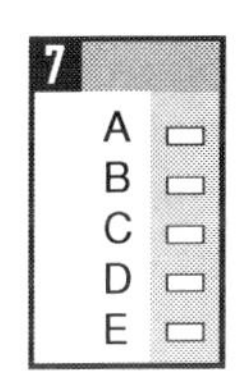
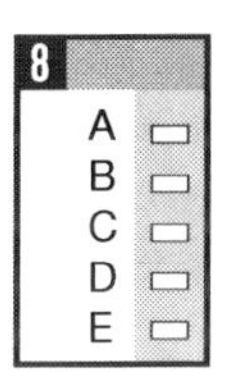
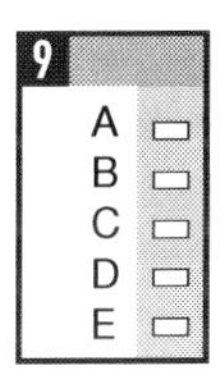

LESSON 7 Improving Your Punctuation Skills: Apostrophes

In this exercise you'll need to spot the punctuation errors in each line of text, as you did in lesson 3. To do this correctly you'll need to have a good understanding of the basic rules of punctuation and when they apply. Let's look at the use of the apostrophe for contraction and possession.

The apostrophe looks like this: '. It's that mark that looks a bit like a floating comma.

Apostrophe of contraction

1 Apostrophes are used for contraction.

Contraction is when we take two words and bang them together to make one word, for example 'Do not' becomes 'Don't.'

To do this, you remove one or more letters, then put an apostrophe in place of those letters to show that you have removed them. This shows readers that two words have been shortened which helps reduce confusion. Let's have a look at some examples.

When you shorten the word not and add it to another you use n't.

Example 1

He was not happy with his meal.
This becomes: He wasn't happy with his meal.

When you shorten the word is you use 's.

Example 2

She is very good at reading.
This becomes: She's very good at reading.

Example 3

You can also remove more than one letter and show that with the apostrophe.

He will watch television tomorrow.
This becomes: He'll watch television tomorrow.

He will becomes He'll so we lose both the w and the i.

Possessive apostrophe

2 Apostrophes are also used to show possession.

Remember that a noun is a person, place or thing (see lesson 3, page 21). In a sentence though, some nouns belong to others. When this happens the noun to which the other noun belongs is called a possessive noun and an apostrophe is used to indicate that possession. Sound confusing? Let's look at some examples!

Example 1

John kicked the boy's football.

In this sentence boy's is a possessive noun and has an apostrophe and s written after it. This shows that the football belongs to the boy.

Example 2

John kicked the boys' football.

In this sentence the apostrophe is after the s. This shows that the football belongs to more than one boy.

Example 3

John kicked Rhys's football.

In this sentence, although the name Rhys already ends with s we can still place an apostrophe and then an s after it. The football belongs to Rhys.

Example 4

John kicked Rhys' football.

It's also possible to simply put an apostrophe after someone's name if it ends with s. Examples 3 and 4 mean the same thing and both are correct ways of using a possessive apostrophe.

LESSON 7 PART 1

My Time

My Score

Now look at the questions below. Work out where capital letters, full stops, and apostrophes have been omitted (left out) and mark your answer (the letter A, B, C or D) on the answer grid. If you think there is no mistake in a particular line then mark option E on the answer grid. You have 10 minutes to complete these.

The new computer: part 1

1 Gareth got a new computer for his birthday. he was so happy he — A B C D — None E

2 ran over to Carls house to tell him the good news. Carl thought it — A B C D — None E

3 was simply wonderful He asked Gareth if he could come and play — A B C D — None E

4 games on it with him. gareth thought that was a great idea and — A B C D — None E

5 asked his friend if he had any games already; but carl did not. — A B C D — None E

6 So they decided to visit their local gaming store to see what they — A B C D — None E

7 had on offer When they arrived they immediately noticed a — A B C D — None E

8 fantastic new game. The games cover was a myriad of colours — A B C D — None E

9 and wonderful strange symbols. the two boys knew they had to — A B C D — None E

10 have it. When they got it home, it really was the best game ever — A B C D — None E

LESSON 7 PART 1: ANSWER SHEET

Mark your answer by putting a horizontal line in one of the boxes for each answer below.

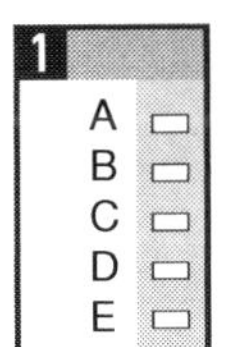

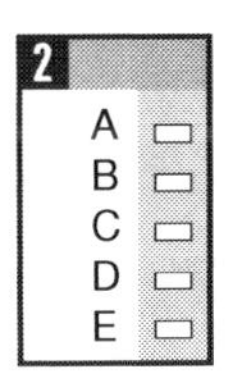

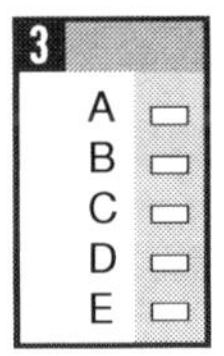

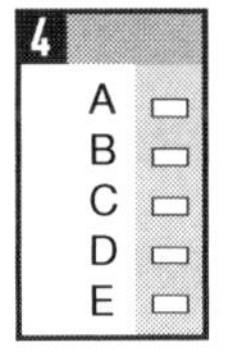

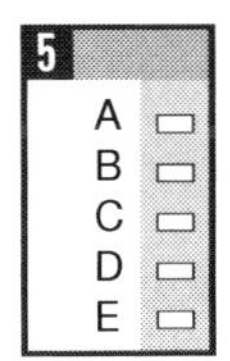

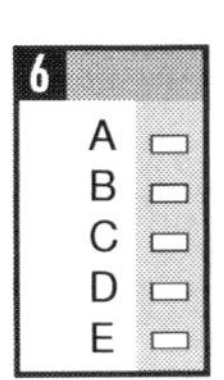

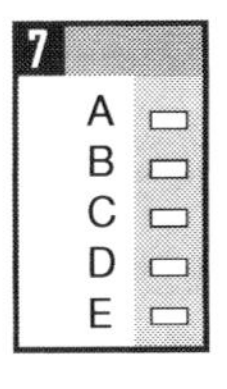

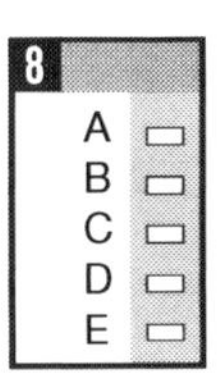

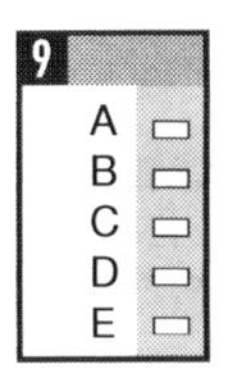

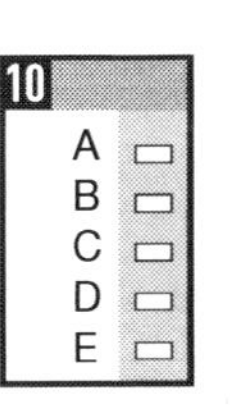

How Did You Do? Let's Find Out!

Here are the correct answers. You may mark your answers to these questions yourself. The answers have the answer letter and its corresponding word so you can clearly see which answer is right.

1	C	He
2	A	Carl's
3	B	wonderful.
4	B	Gareth
5	D	Carl
6	E	none
7	A	offer.
8	B	game's
9	C	The
10	D	ever.

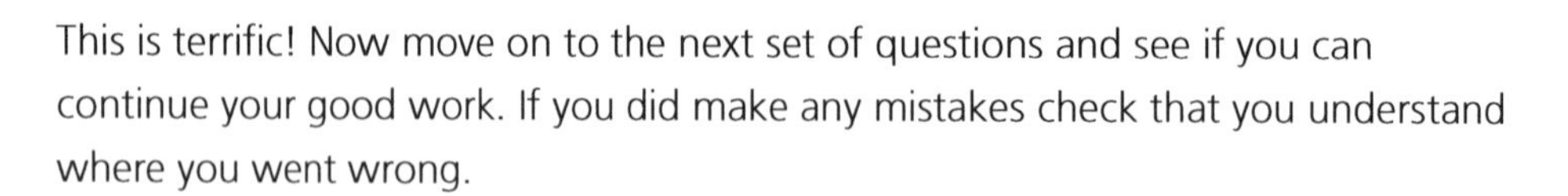

If you scored 8 or more out of 10

This is terrific! Now move on to the next set of questions and see if you can continue your good work. If you did make any mistakes check that you understand where you went wrong.

If you scored 6 or 7 out of 10 

Make sure that you read the complete sentences and take a lot of care when thinking about where an apostrophe, a full stop or a capital letter should go. Look back at the earlier lessons to make sure you understand each one.

If you scored 5 or fewer out of 10 

Read the suggestions that follow before moving on to the next set of questions.

➪ Make sure you understand exactly where apostrophes, full stops and capital letters should be used.

➪ Practise hard using the earlier examples so that you understand how to use the apostrophe properly – this is a very tricky area of punctuation.

LESSON 7 PART 2

My Time

My Score

Now let's try some more. Work out where capital letters, full stops, and apostrophes have been left out and mark your answer (the letter A, B, C or D) on the answer grid. If you think there are no mistakes in a particular line then mark option E on the answer grid. You have 10 minutes to complete these. Ask an adult to mark these for you. Then write your time and score in the box at the top.

The new computer: part 2

1 Gareth and carl were at home one day playing on Gareth's

A	B	C	D	None E
Gareth and carl	were at home	one day playing	on Gareth's	

2 computer It was a racing car game and both boys thought it was

A	B	C	D	None E
computer It	was a racing car	game and both boys	thought it was	

3 brilliant. 'This is the best game i've ever played!' said Gareth to

A	B	C	D	None E
brilliant. 'This	is the best game	i've ever played!'	said Gareth to	

4 his friend. 'Yes its fantastic!' agreed Carl, 'The cars move so

A	B	C	D	None E
his friend. 'Yes	its fantastic!'	agreed Carl, 'The	cars move so	

5 quickly that it makes it really exciting' The boys played their

A	B	C	D	None E
quickly that it	makes it really	exciting' The	boys played their	

6 game all day, racing their cars round the tracks and making them

A	B	C	D	None E
game all day,	racing their cars	round the tracks	and making them	

7 go faster and faster. eventually it was time for Carl to go home

A	B	C	D	None E
go faster and	faster. eventually	it was time for	Carl to go home	

8 so he waved goodbye to Gareth and skipped home happily He

A	B	C	D	None E
so he waved	goodbye to Gareth	and skipped	home happily He	

9 had really enjoyed seeing his best friend again. gareth had

A	B	C	D	None E
had really enjoyed	seeing his best	friend again.	gareth had	

10 enjoyed it too – after all its more fun sharing your games.

A	B	C	D	None E
enjoyed it too –	after all its	more fun sharing	your games.	

LESSON 7 PART 2: ANSWER SHEET

Mark your answer by putting a horizontal line in one of the boxes for each question below.

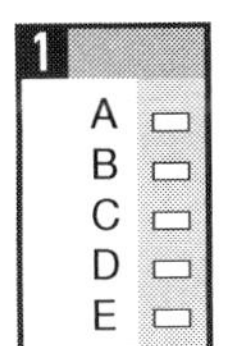

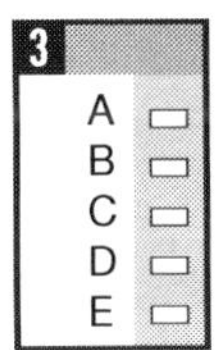

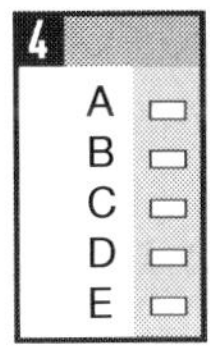

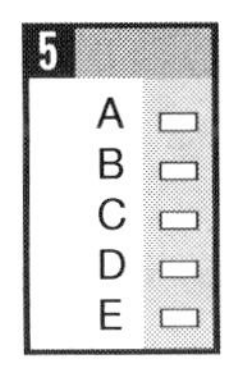

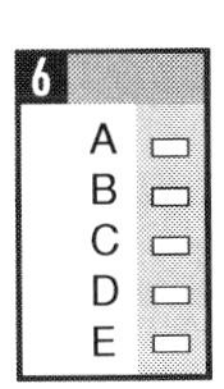

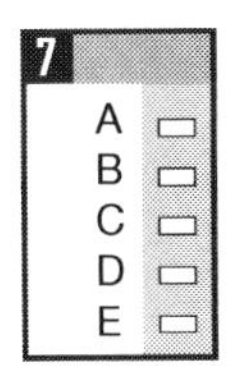

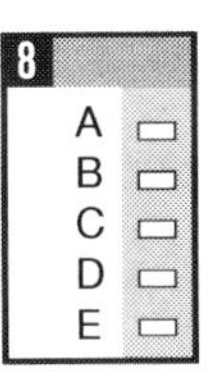

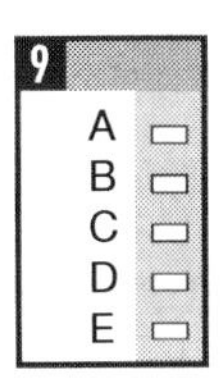

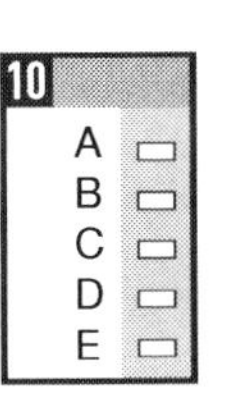

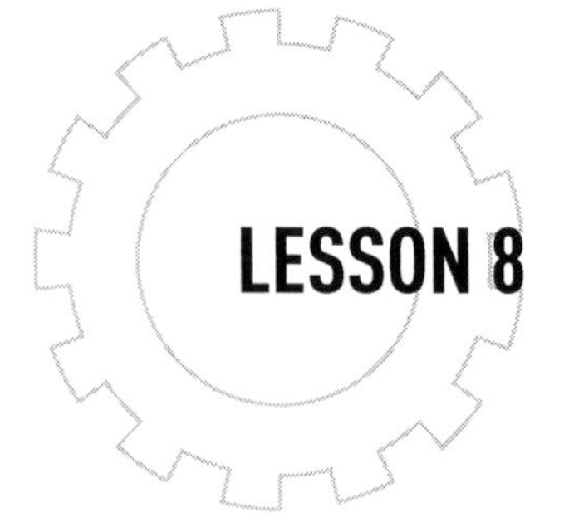

LESSON 8 Practising Comprehension and Grammar

In this exercise you'll read a passage of text and then answer some questions about it. Remember, as in lesson 4 you'll be asked a mixture of comprehension and grammar questions.

A Improving Your Comprehension: Analytical Questions

To do well at comprehension questions it's important that you recognise the style of question you are being asked. Here we'll look at analytical questions.

Typically these questions ask you to analyse what you've read. Let's look at an example.

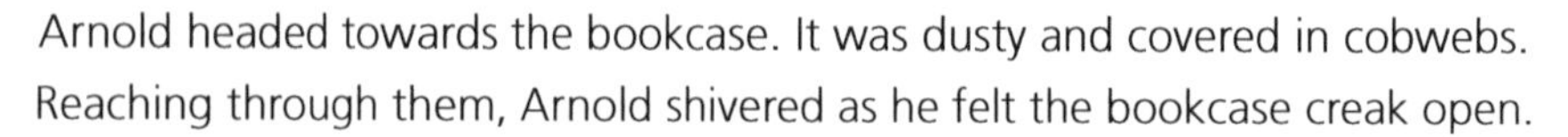

Example

Arnold headed towards the bookcase. It was dusty and covered in cobwebs. Reaching through them, Arnold shivered as he felt the bookcase creak open.

1 Why did Arnold shiver?

A he was cold
B the bookcase was cold
C he was not wearing a coat
D he was nervous
E he was brave

The answer to the question above is D – he was nervous. Although it's possible that Arnold was cold, we are told that he shivered when the bookcase creaked open. It would follow then that this is because bookcases do not usually open with a creak and this unsettled him in some way. Remember to look for clues when answering these types of questions and don't simply choose the obvious answer.

Questions for comprehension skills follow the next part of this lesson, which is on grammar skills.

B Improving Your Grammar: Adverbs

Here we'll look at different types of adverbs, which you need to know really well.

Adverbs tell us how, where or when something happens.

There are several different types of adverb. Adverbs of manner tell us how something was done. Let's look at an example.

Example 

John skilfully kicked the football.

In this sentence the adverb skilfully tells us how John kicked the football and so it's an adverb of manner. Adverbs of manner often end with 'ly' but not always.

Now look at the sentences below. Underline the adverb of manner in each.

1. The dog chewed patiently on a bone.
2. The new restaurant joyously opened its doors for the first time.
3. Yesterday the rain was falling heavily.
4. White clouds are gathering ominously over London.
5. The squirrel climbed the tree dextrously with a nut in its mouth.
6. The beautiful painting in the gold frame hung safely in the lounge.
7. Many people queued expectantly for the sale.
8. I played well for my football team.
9. The children played happily on the swings, slide and roundabout.
10. The snowy white owl perched precariously in the tree.

Answers: 1. patiently, 2. joyously, 3. heavily, 4. ominously, 5. dextrously, 6. safely, 7. expectantly, 8. well, 9. happily, 10. precariously

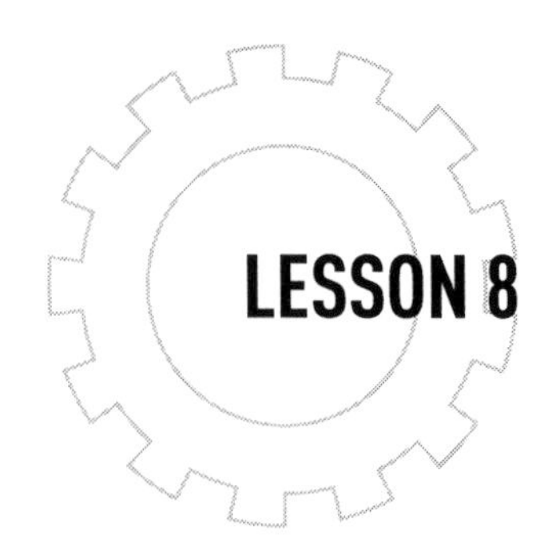

LESSON 8 Practice Questions

My Time | **My Score**

Now read the passage below carefully and then answer the questions that follow. They may be comprehension or grammar questions. Some questions might cover what you learned in lesson 4 as well. When you think you've worked out the correct answer, mark its letter on the answer grid on page 63. Ask an adult to mark your answers. You should be able to complete this task in about 10 minutes, which includes the time you have to read the passage.

The chameleon stone

In the excerpt that follows, a young farmer's boy, Tanon, discovers a strange stone, which seems to have magical properties.

1 It felt cold to touch. Well, not exactly cold, more cool and smooth. What Tanon could not understand was what it was doing here – in the cattle shed. How did it get here?

2 It was fashioned like no other stone that Tanon had ever seen. He was fascinated by it and it held his gaze like a venomous snake did its prey, just before making its lethal strike. Yet there was no strike – just the beautiful curves of this most precious of objects.

3 At least, Tanon presumed it was precious, but now he had a decision to make. Should he take it immediately to his master or could he hold on to its smoothness for just a little longer?

4 A clap of thunder broke his daydream and he turned his gaze heavenwards. Dark clouds were forming like smoke billowing from an open fire and Tanon knew he had not much time before the rain came. He had to get the cattle inside before the full force of the storm came to bear down on the farm.

5 Just as he was standing up, his prize started to change. Swirling mists and patterns drifted over its outer layer and a pale pulsing light seemed to throb from its core. Tanon stared in wonder – was this some sort of magical object?

1 Why do you think Tanon was surprised to find the stone in the cattle shed? (paragraph 1)

A because he had dropped the stone somewhere else

B because the stone belonged to his master

C because he had stolen the stone

D because the stone looked out of place in the cattle shed

E because it was just a stone

2 'Venomous' is what part of speech? (paragraph 2)

A verb

B noun

C adverb

D adjective

E proper noun

3 In the phrase 'lethal strike…', lethal is what part of speech? (paragraph 2)

A verb

B adverb

C noun

D pronoun

E adjective

4 What decision did Tanon have to make? (paragraph 3)

A whether or not to keep the stone for himself

B where he should hide the stone

C whether or not to take the cattle into their shed

D who to take the stone to

E whether or not it would rain

5 'Immediately' is what part of speech? (paragraph 3)

A adverb

B adjective

C noun

D preposition

E verb

6 'Master' is an example of? (paragraph 3)

A adverb

B adjective

C noun

D preposition

E verb

7 In the phrase 'open fire', 'open' is an example of? (paragraph 4)

A adverb

B adjective

C noun

D preposition

E verb

8 Why did Tanon look towards the sky? (paragraph 4)

A he was looking at the trees

B he wanted to watch the rain

C he wanted to see how long it would be before it rained

D he wanted to see the lightning

E it was getting dark

9 'Swirling' is an example of? (paragraph 5)

A conjunction

B verb

C noun

D adverb

E adjective

10 'Core' is an example of? (paragraph 5)

A verb

B adverb

C adjective

D pronoun

E noun

LESSON 8 PART 3: ANSWER SHEET

Mark your answer by putting a horizontal line in one of the boxes as in the example below.

Example:

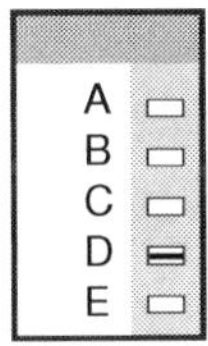

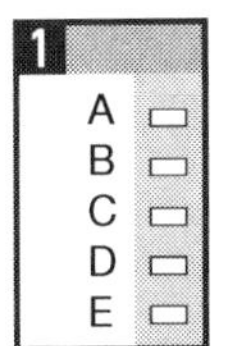

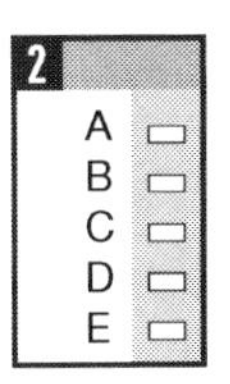

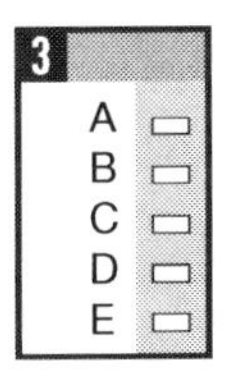

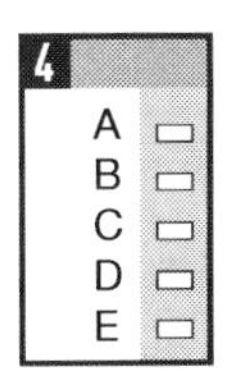

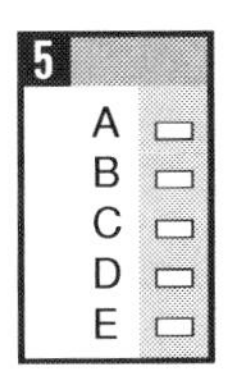

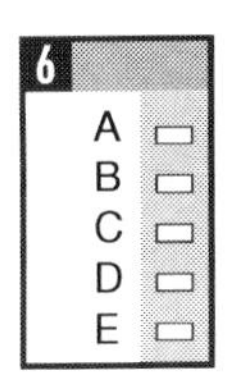

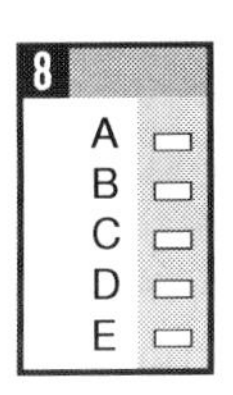

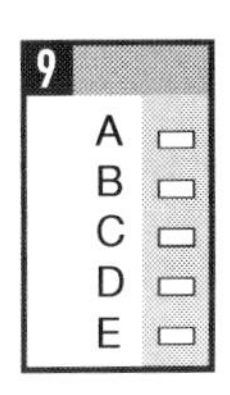

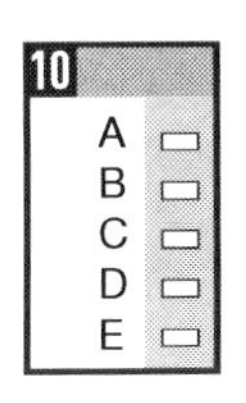

SECTION 3

LESSON 9 Improving Your Spelling Skills

As in lessons 1 and 5, you'll be looking at words that are spelled incorrectly and words that are misused. Let's look at some further examples.

Word	Meaning	Clue
practice	This is the noun and spelled with a 'c'– 'He went to football practice'.	
practise	This is the verb and spelled with an 's'– 'She practises the violin'.	
desert	When used as a noun = hot, dry, sandy place. When used as a verb = to abandon or leave someone.	
dessert	A pudding or something sweet after a meal.	I remember this one by having the two 's' stand for something sweet.
rain	The wet stuff that falls from the sky!	
reign	What a king or queen does over their subjects.	
rein	A leather strap used by a rider to control a horse.	
vain	This can either mean someone cares too much about their appearance or when something is unsuccessful or produces no result.	
vein	Carries blood in our bodies.	
vane	As in a weather vane that indicates the direction of the wind.	

Make sure you learn the spellings above before you try the practice questions.

By now you should know what to do for this type of question, but I've given an example here just to remind you. Remember that if you see a word which seems as though it's spelled correctly but is used in the wrong way that counts as a spelling mistake. Let's look at the example.

Example

The children	walked	sensibly two	the shops.	None
A	B	C	D	E

In the sentence above you can see that the word 'two' is spelled correctly but it's the wrong word here as it has been used in the wrong context. 'Two' means the number of objects and can't be used as it is in the sentence above. This word is in the group labelled C so you need to mark C on the answer sheet. The correct word to use here is 'to'.

If you think that all the words are spelled correctly in the sentence you'll need to mark E which is under the word 'None'.

HELPFUL HINTS

- There are no grammatical mistakes in these questions.
- There are no words missing in these questions – if you think the sentence doesn't make sense you'll need to read it again.
- Make sure that you read each sentence fully to gain the correct context. Some sentences go on to the next line so you watch out for these.

LESSON 9 PART 1

My Time

My Score

Now look at the questions below. Work out where there are misspellings or correctly spelled but wrongly used words. Then mark your answer (the letter A, B, C or D) on the answer grid. If you think there are no mistakes in a particular question mark option E on the answer grid. You have 10 minutes to complete these.

The race: part 1

	A	B	C	D	E
1	Kalifa looked	behind him as	he sped across	the dessert. The	None
2	other riders	were pulling	hard on the rains	of their horses but	None
3	it seemed to	be in vein as	Kalifa continued	to pull away from	None
4	them. Dark	clouds gathered	in the distance	and Kalifa hoped	None
5	he would finish	the race before	the reign came	down. He	None
6	urged his horse	to go faster.	All the practice	that he had done	None
7	over the past	twelve months	was helping	him no as he rode	None
8	towards the finish.	There it was!	Kalifa could	see the too	None
9	white tents	that marked the	finish line.	A quick glance bak	None
10	told him	that he would	win the race	this year.	None

LESSON 9 PART 1: ANSWER SHEET

Mark your answer by putting a horizontal line in one of the boxes as in the example below.

Example:

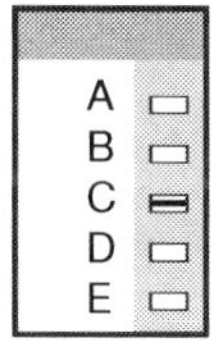

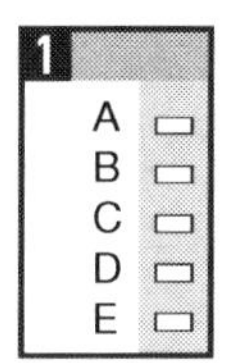
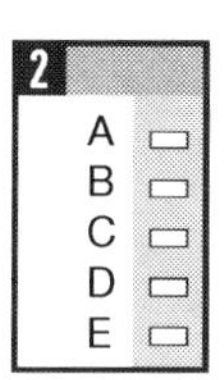
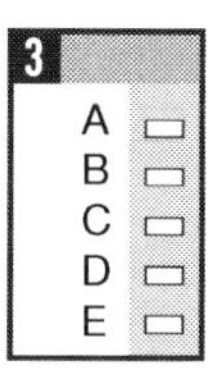
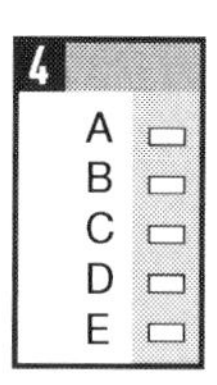
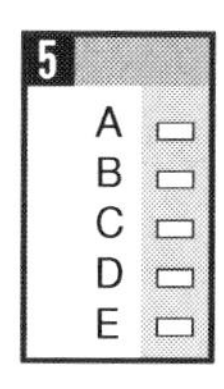

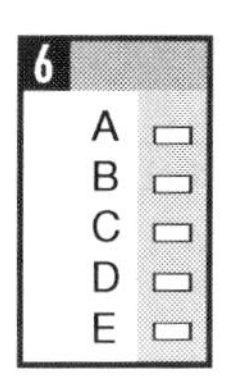

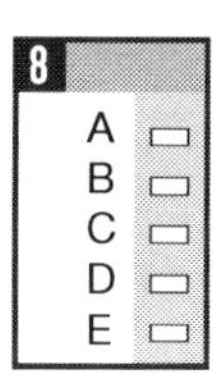

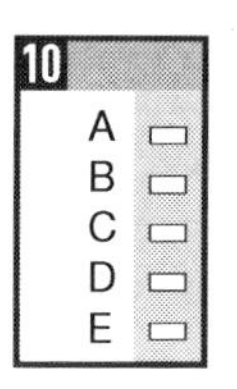

How Did You Do? Let's Find Out!

Here are the correct answers. You may mark your answers to these questions yourself. You will see the answer letter, the word that was spelled incorrectly and the correct spelling in brackets so you can understand why the answers are correct.

1 D dessert (desert)

2 C rains (reins)

3 B vein (vain)

4 E none

5 C reign (rain)

6 C practice (practise)

7 D no (now)

8 D too (two)

9 D bak (back)

10 E none

If you scored 8 or more out of 10

A great score – well done! Now move on to the next set of questions and see if you can continue your good work.

If you scored 5 to 7 out of 10

Read this advice with an adult before moving on to the next set of questions.

➪ Look at the answers. You should know all of the words and know how to use them. If you don't, go back and look at the spelling skills tables on pages 4, 34 and 64 to make sure you know and understand all of the words.

➪ Did you notice that many of the questions had words that were used in the wrong context? This counts as a spelling mistake and you needed to choose the part of the sentence that contained that word as your answer.

➪ Make sure you read the entire sentence, not just a line – that way you'll understand the context and hopefully know which word is being used incorrectly!

If you scored fewer than 5 out of 10

Fewer than 5 is a score you will need to improve. Read the suggestions that follow before moving on to the next set of questions.

➪ If you don't understand the questions, ask an adult to read the instructions and go through the example with you again. Then take another look at your answers and see if you can correct them.

➪ Keep using the spelling skills tables on pages 4, 34 and 64 to help you recognise misspellings and understand the different contexts in which words should be used.

➪ Use the vocabulary builders on page 125 to help you learn new words.

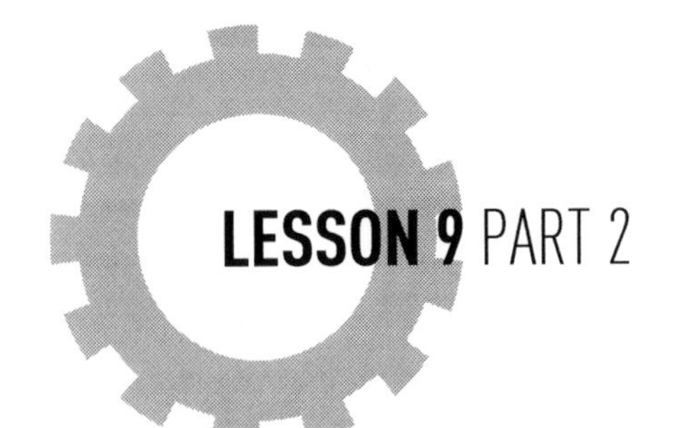

LESSON 9 PART 2

My Time

My Score

Now let's try some more. Work out where there are misspellings and wrongly used words and mark your answer (the letter A, B, C or D) on the answer grid. If you think there are no mistakes in a particular line then mark option E on the answer grid. You have 10 minutes to complete these.

The race: part 2

	A	B	C	D	None (E)
1	As Kalifa crossed	the finnish line	flags waved	to show him	
2	that he had	been victourious.	His horse seemed happy	too, but it	
3	was panting	heavily and beeds	of sweat were	rolling down its	
4	flanks. Kalifa	pulled sharpely	on the reins	and his horse	
5	stopped. He vaulted	off its back and led	it to water	so it could	
6	quench its thirst.	People started	to approche	him and cheer.	
7	He was the	youngest boy ever	to win the	desert horse race.	
8	To his village,	Kalifa would be	seen as a heroe.	Yet he was	
9	a shye	boy and didn't	know what to	say to those who greeted	
10	him with	such unbridled	enthusiasm and	abject delite.	

LESSON 9 PART 2: ANSWER SHEET

Mark your answer by putting a horizontal line in one of the boxes as in the example below.

Example:

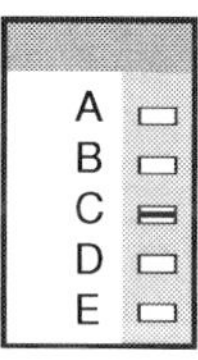

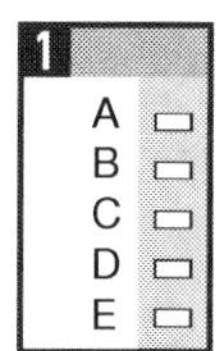

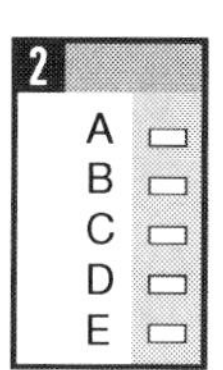

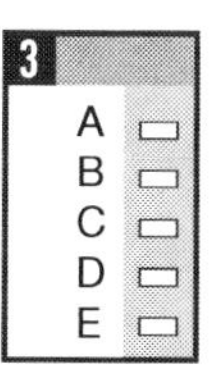

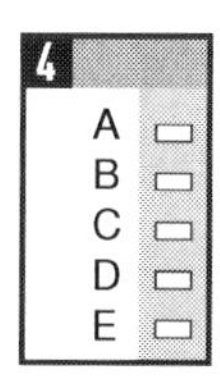

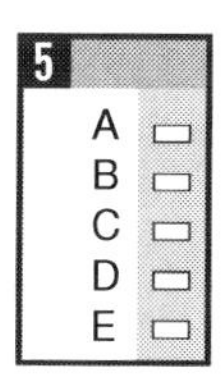

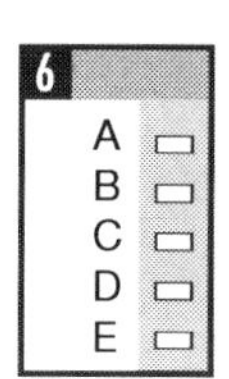

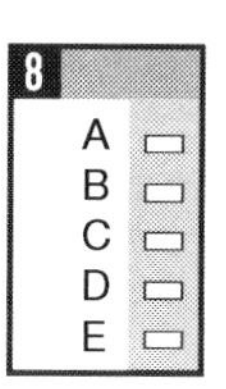

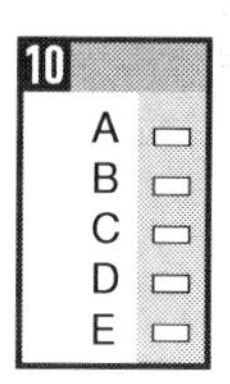

LESSON 10 Understanding Sentence Structure

In this exercise you're asked the same kind of question that you've already answered in lessons 2 and 6.

Before you start, you need to know that verbs should agree with their subject. For example: 'The boys plays happily on the field'. This sentence is not correct because there is more than one boy and the verb ending 'plays' is for just one boy. 'The sentence should read: 'The boys <u>play</u> happily on the field'.

Let's look at more examples.

Example 1

The children [was] [were] [will] [is] [woz] playing on the swings.

	A	B	C	D	E	
The children	was	were	will	is	woz	playing on the swings.

In the example above you must remember that 'children' is plural – that means there is more than one of them! So you can't use the words 'was' or 'is' as you would use these with one 'child'. The correct answer is 'were' so you need to mark <u>B</u> on the answer sheet. If you read the sentence back to yourself, 'were' is the only word which helps the sentence makes sense.

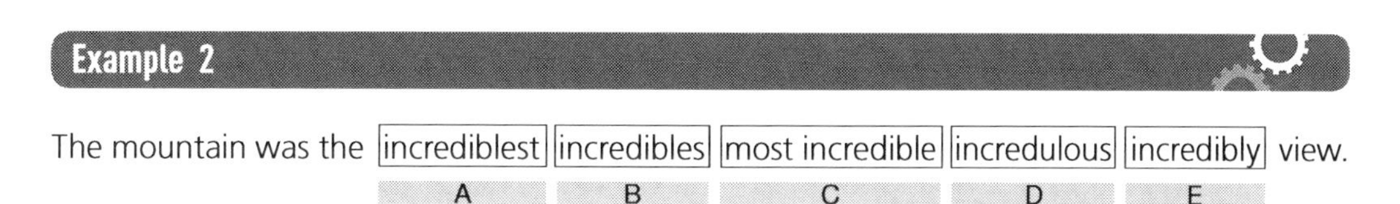

Example 2

	A	B	C	D	E	
The mountain was the	incrediblest	incredibles	most incredible	incredulous	incredibly	view.

The answer to the question above is <u>most incredible</u> so you'll need to mark <u>C</u> on the answer sheet. It doesn't matter that this answer has two words provided it makes sense!

LESSON 10 PART 1

My Time

My Score

Now look at the questions below. Work out which word will complete each sentence so that it makes sense. Then mark your answer (the letter A, B, C, D or E) on the answer grid. You have 10 minutes to complete these.

At the beach: part 1

1 Kai, Vera and [there] [their] [they're] [the] [them] parents went
(A there, B their, C they're, D the, E them)

2 [too] [two] [to] [tow] [toe] the beach because it was
(A too, B two, C to, D tow, E toe)

3 so sunny. 'I hope it doesn't [rain] [reign] [rein] [rane] [rayne]',
(A rain, B reign, C rein, D rane, E rayne)

4 said Vera. But the sun [shines] [shone] [shining] [shoned] [shonne]
(A shines, B shone, C shining, D shoned, E shonne)

5 down and they all [swims] [swim] [swams] [swam] [swimming]
(A swims, B swim, C swams, D swam, E swimming)

6 happily in the [see] [sea] [seen] [cea] [sae.] Then they sat down and
(A see, B sea, C seen, D cea, E sae.)

7 [ate] [eat] [eight] [et] [eats] a lovely picnic. Kai remarked, 'The beach
(A ate, B eat, C eight, D et, E eats)

8 is just like a [dessert] [dezert] [deserte] [desserte] [desert] because there
(A dessert, B dezert, C deserte, D desserte, E desert)

9 is so much sand. I will [practice] [practiss] [practise] [practis] [practic] making sand castles
(A practice, B practiss, C practise, D practis, E practic)

10 so they will be the [amazingly] [amazingest] [most amazing] [more amazing] [amazing]
(A amazingly, B amazingest, C most amazing, D more amazing, E amazing)

structures ever.

LESSON 10 PART 1: ANSWER SHEET

Mark your answer by putting a horizontal line in one of the boxes as in the examples below.

Example 1:

A
B
C
D
E

Example 2:

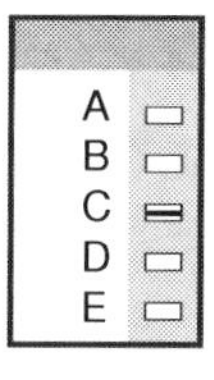

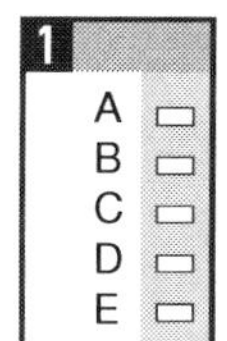

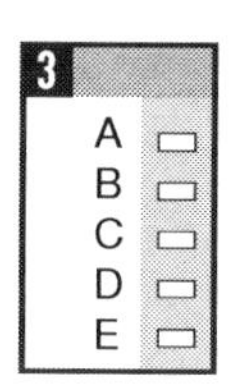

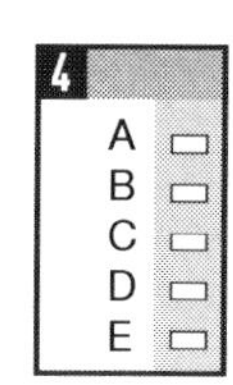

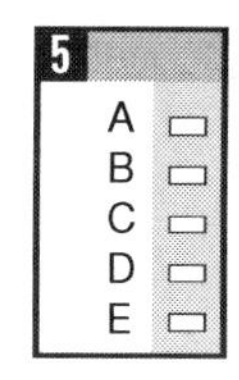

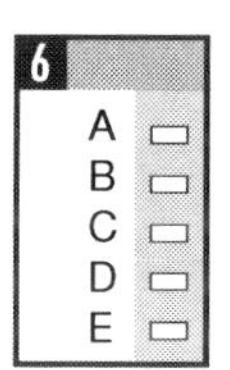

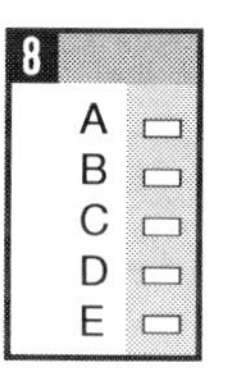

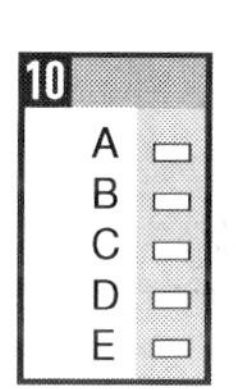

How Did You Do? Let's Find Out!

Here are the correct answers. You may mark your answers to these questions yourself. I've written the answer letter and word, just so you know!

1 B their

2 C to

3 A rain

4 B shone

5 D swam

6 B sea

7 A ate

8 E desert

9 C practise

10 C most amazing

If you scored 8 or more out of 10

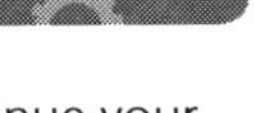

Well done! Move on to the next set of questions and see if you can continue your good work.

If you scored 5 to 7 out of 10

Take some time to read the following advice with an adult before moving on to the next set of questions.

Look at the answers. You should know the words and understand when they should be used. If you don't, go back and look at the spelling skills tables on pages 4, 34 and 64 and use it to learn them. If the words aren't on the spelling sheet then use the vocabulary builders on page 125. Write the words down and look them up in a dictionary so you'll know them in future.

If you scored fewer than 5 out of 10

You need to improve this score. To do this read the suggestions below before moving on to the next set of questions.

➪ Do you understand what you have to do? If not, ask an adult to read the instructions and go through the example with you again. Then take another look at your answers and see if you can correct them.

➪ Use the vocabulary builders on page 125 to help you with new words.

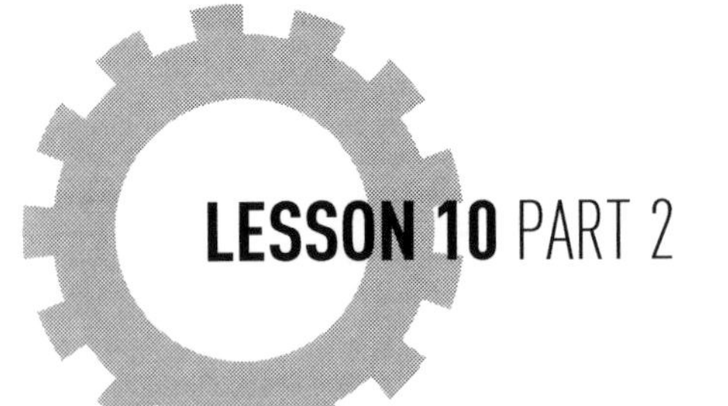

LESSON 10 PART 2

My Time

My Score

Now let's try some more. Work out which word will complete each sentence so that it makes sense, making sure that it both makes sense and is spelled correctly. Then mark your answer (the letter A, B, C, D or E) on the answer grid. You have 10 minutes to complete this task. Ask an adult to mark these for you.

At the beach: part 2

1 Kai finished [build | builded | built | building | billding] his sand castle
A = build, B = builded, C = built, D = building, E = billding

2 by placing a flag on top. He looked up and [sure | sawe | saw | sore | soor]
A = sure, B = sawe, C = saw, D = sore, E = soor

3 waves from the [see | cee | sae | cea | sea] getting closer and closer. He
A = see, B = cee, C = sae, D = cea, E = sea

4 started [dig | dug | digged | digging | dugging] out sand for a new wall, but
A = dig, B = dug, C = digged, D = digging, E = dugging

5 the waves [were | ware | wore | where | we're] getting higher and his new
A = were, B = ware, C = wore, D = where, E = we're

6 wall [would | wood | wud | wered | word] not be ready in time. Just then he
A = would, B = wood, C = wud, D = wered, E = word

7 looked up as another [pare | pear | pair | paire | peer] of hands joined his and
A = pare, B = pear, C = pair, D = paire, E = peer

8 helped pile the sand up [hi | hire | hie | high | highe]. It was his sister Vera.
A = hi, B = hire, C = hie, D = high, E = highe

9 She had arrived just in time! The waves [come | came | caim | cam | coming]
A = come, B = came, C = caim, D = cam, E = coming

10 crashing in but the new wall [saived | save | saving | saved | sayved] his castle!
A = saived, B = save, C = saving, D = saved, E = sayved

LESSON 10 PART 2: ANSWER SHEET

Mark your answer by putting a horizontal line in one of the boxes as in the examples below.

Example 1:

A
B
C
D
E

Example 2:

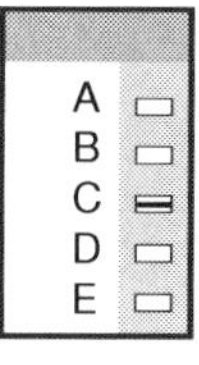

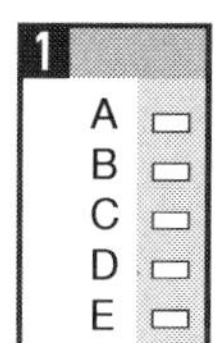

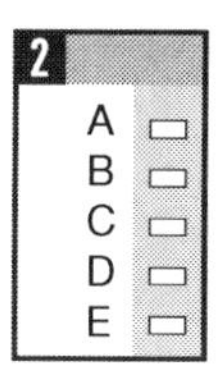

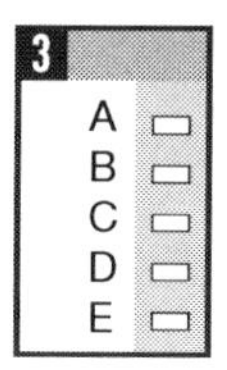

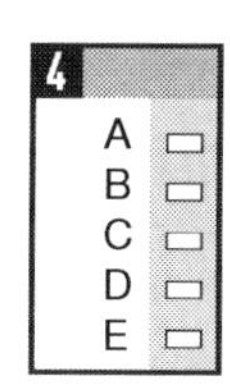

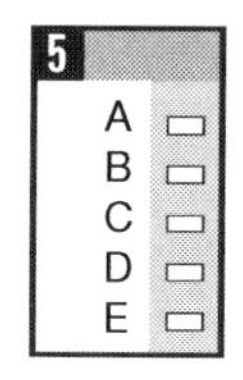

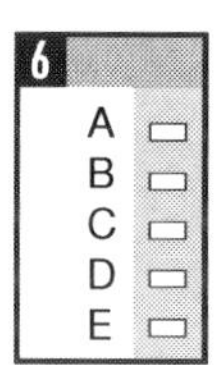

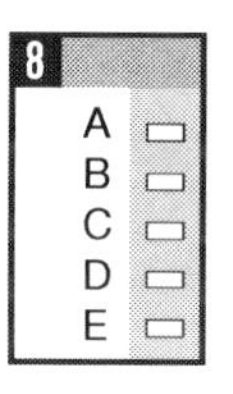

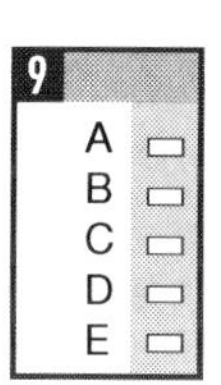

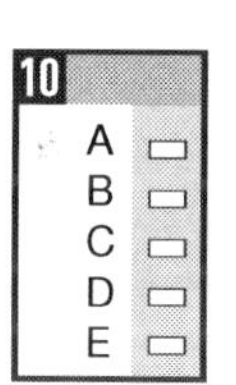

LESSON 11 Improving Your Punctuation Skills: Question Marks and Commas

In this exercise you'll need to spot the punctuation errors in each question. To do this correctly you'll need to have a good understanding of the basic rules of punctuation and when they apply. Let's look at the use of the question mark and the comma.

The question mark

Whenever a question is asked in a sentence, the question mark must be used at the end of it.

Example 1

Can we go to the cinema

This becomes: Can we go to the <u>cinema?</u>

If a question is asked in direct speech, make sure the question mark goes at the end of the question and <u>not</u> the end of the sentence. Simply place a full stop at the end of the sentence as usual.

Example 2

'Do you have a pencil' asked the teacher

This becomes: 'Do you have a <u>pencil?'</u> asked the <u>teacher.</u>

The comma

Now this one can be a bit tricky. It is important to remember that you'll be taking a test and there must be a definite correct answer but some experts are still debating when and where exactly commas should be used! So my advice to students is that unless you're absolutely certain a comma is missing, don't put one in. If in doubt – leave it out! So where do we know commas must be used? The answer to this is – in lists.

When three or more objects are listed then a comma should be used to separate them.

Example 3

He went shopping and bought bread milk sugar and eggs.

This becomes: He went shopping and bought <u>bread,</u> <u>milk,</u> sugar and eggs.

Note how there is no comma between the last two items since the word <u>and</u> links these.

LESSON 11 PART 1

My Time

My Score

Now look at the questions below. Work out where question marks, capital letters, full stops and apostrophes have been omitted (left out) and mark your answer (the letter A, B, C or D) on the answer grid. If you think there is no mistake in a particular line then mark option E on the answer grid. You have 10 minutes to complete this test.

The steam train: part 1

1. as the children stood excitedly on the platform, they heard the — A B C D — None E
2. sound of the steam train. Then they heard its whistle and — A B C D — None E
3. started jumping up and down 'There it is,' shouted one child — A B C D — None E
4. as the train came into view. 'Its magnificent,' cried another. — A B C D — None E
5. The train came to a slow halt and everyone clambered — A B C D — None E
6. aboard There were shouts of joy and delight from all the — A B C D — None E
7. children. 'Have you been on a steam train before' asked — A B C D — None E
8. the driver. They all shook their heads. 'then this will be very — A B C D — None E
9. special for you all,' the driver continued. 'sit down everyone — A B C D — None E
10. and get ready for a wonderful steam train journey' — A B C D — None E

LESSON 11 PART 1: ANSWER SHEET

Mark your answer by putting a horizontal line in one of the boxes for each answer below.

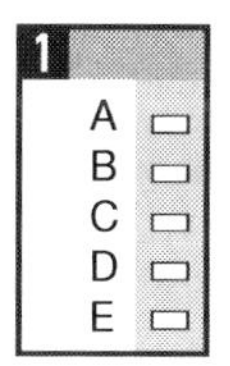

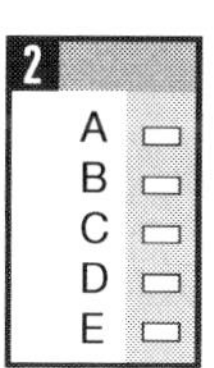

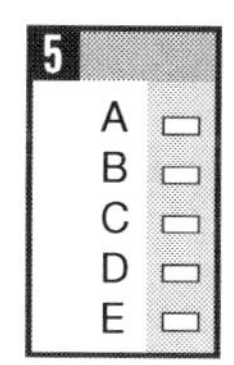

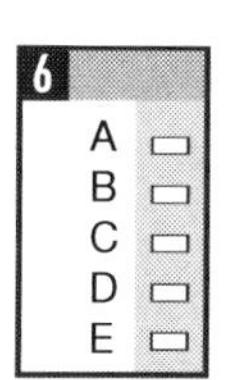

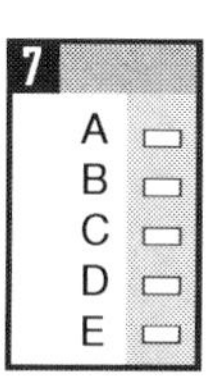

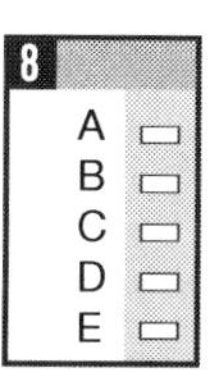

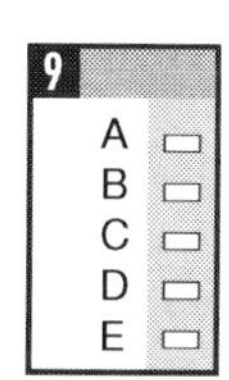

How Did You Do? Let's Find Out!

Here are the correct answers. You may mark your answers to these questions yourself. I've written the answer letter and the correct punctuation or capital letters so you can follow and understand each answer.

1	A	As
2	E	none
3	B	down.
4	C	It's
5	E	none
6	A	aboard.
7	D	before?'
8	C	'Then
9	D	'Sit
10	D	journey.'

If you scored 8 or more out of 10

This is great! Move on to the next set of questions and see if you can continue your good work. But take a look at where you went wrong so you can get it right next time.

If you scored 6 or 7 out of 10

Make sure that you read complete sentences and take lots of care when thinking about where an apostrophe, question mark, comma, full stop or capital letter should go.

If you scored 5 or fewer out of 10

This is quite a low score but with some hard work you can improve it. Read the suggestions that follow before moving on to the next set of questions.

- ➪ If you had trouble understanding how to answer the questions get an adult to read through the instructions with you. Then take another look at your answers and see if you can correct them.

- ➪ Make sure you clearly understand where exactly full stops and capital letters should be used. You really must be strong on these before you move on.

- ➪ Make sure you read each sentence and look for those that are asking questions. That way you'll know when to put in a missing question mark.

LESSON 11 PART 2

My Time

My Score

Now let's try some more. Work out where question marks, commas, capital letters, full stops and apostrophes have been omitted (left out) and mark your answer (the letter A, B, C or D) on the answer grid. If you think there are no mistakes in a particular line then mark option E on the answer grid. You have 10 minutes to complete these. Ask an adult to mark these for you.

The steam train: part 2

	A	B	C	D	None
1	Then they heard	the guards whistle	and saw him	wave his	E
2	green flag	The train slowly	pulled out of	the station amid	E
3	clouds of smoke.	'What's that'	asked one child	pointing to	E
4	a strange	looking tower	by the side of the	track. 'that's a	E
5	water tower,'	said the guard,	'Its where we get	water for the	E
6	train.' as	it began to pick	up speed	the children saw many	E
7	things flashing	past their windows.	They saw	fields sheep	E
8	and many	interesting	small cottages.	Just then something else	E
9	came into view	and the guard	pointed to it	'Look at that,' he	E
10	said, 'It's a	lighthouse, it	helps ships when	they are at sea'	E

LESSON 11 PART 2: ANSWER SHEET

Mark your answer by putting a horizontal line in one of the boxes for each answer below.

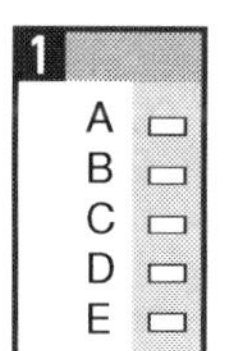

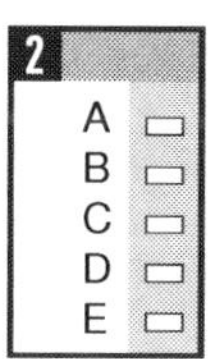

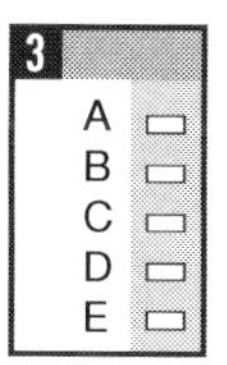

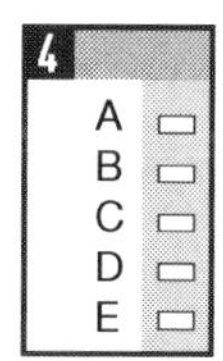

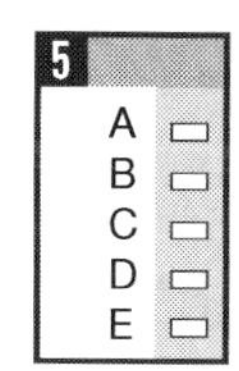

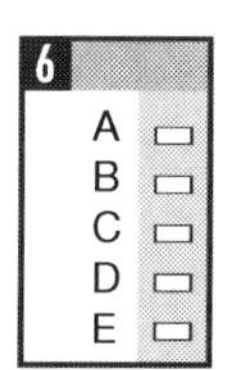

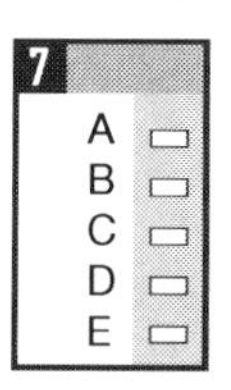

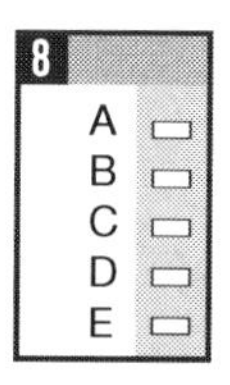

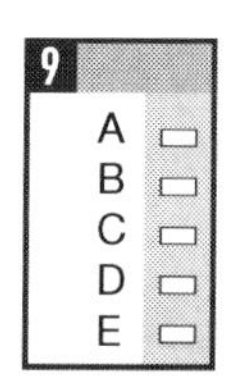

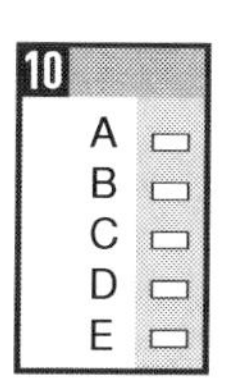

LESSON 12 Practising Comprehension and Grammar

In this exercise you'll read a passage of text and then answer some questions about it. Remember that you'll be asked a mixture of comprehension and grammar questions.

A Improving Your Comprehension: Key Vocabulary and Phrases

To do well at comprehension questions it's important that you recognise the style of question you are being asked. Here we'll look at questions that require you to find a particular word or phrase.

With these questions you'll need to think carefully about the one word – or phrase if you're asked for that – which gives the meaning described in the question. Let's look at an example.

Example

Arnold headed towards the bookcase. It was dusty and covered in cobwebs. Reaching through them, Arnold's fingers trembled as he felt the bookcase creak open.

1 Which word in the passage tells you that Arnold was nervous?

A covered
B cobwebs
C trembled
D creak
E dusty

The answer to the question above is C – trembled. This is a word that describes shaking when we are nervous.

One way you can help yourself do well at these questions is by reading from a book every night. That way you'll expand your vocabulary quickly.

Questions for comprehension skills follow the next part of this lesson, which is on grammar skills.

B Improving Your Grammar: Collective Nouns

Here you'll try to tackle some of the more common types of grammar problems which you need to know. For this lesson we'll look at collective nouns.

Collective nouns are words used to describe a group of nouns.

For example, 52 cards would be known as a pack of cards. Collective nouns take a singular verb unless there is more than one of them.

Example

A crowd of onlookers surrounded the injured person.

In this sentence there is only one collective noun – the crowd.

Underline the collective noun in each sentence below.

1. Swimming in the shallow water was a shoal of herrings.
2. In the field, happily grazing, was a flock of sheep.
3. All night we could hear the pack of wolves howling.
4. Looking out to sea, we noticed a pod of dolphins swimming.
5. The pride of lions slept all day on the African plains.
6. A long flight of steps led to the top of the tower.
7. Our cat has just had a litter of seven kittens.
8. We picked several bunches of juicy grapes from the vine.
9. The hen waddled by with her brood of chicks.
10. A band of thieves stole the precious diamonds.

Answers: 1. shoal, 2. flock, 3. pack, 4. pod, 5. pride, 6. flight, 7. litter, 8. bunches, 9. brood, 10. band

LESSON 12 Practice Questions

My Time

My Score

Now read the passage below carefully and answer the questions that follow. They may be comprehension or grammar questions. There may also be questions about things you have learned in other lessons. When you've worked out the correct answer, mark your answer on the answer grid on page 93. Ask an adult to mark your answers for you. You should be able to complete this test in about 10 minutes, which includes the time you have to read the passage.

Caged

In the excerpt that follows, a group of children has won a day helping the keepers at a zoo. Two of the children have gone missing, along with the zoo's tigers.

1 Bria was the first to speak. 'I knew we shouldn't have left them on their own,' she growled. By 'them' she meant Rod and Betty, two of her classmates. They had been assigned cleaning duties at the tiger enclosure, and had clearly forgotten one basic rule of the job: shut the cage with the tigers on the inside!

2 Tim, who had turned as white as a ghost, was shaking as he spoke. 'Forget whether or not we should have trusted them,' he was almost screaming now as his voice became high pitched, 'where are the tigers?'

3 The question hit them like a battering ram and Toby, who was the youngest, began whimpering as he realised what danger they might be in. They all stood, unmoving, as though some kind of invisible force held them in place.

4 'What do we do now?' Bria whispered, daring to break the unnerving silence and hoping deep down in her heart that the tigers were not listening in to their conversation.

5 'Dunno,' Tim murmured.

6 Toby began sobbing big, terrified tears and pointed towards the open cage with a quivering finger. The others stared as he began shuffling in the same direction. It seemed like an eternity before he reached the cage and stepped inside. Between sobs he gasped to the others, 'H-hurry!'

7 The pair had no idea what was happening but couldn't leave their friend so they quickly tiptoed across to where he shook by the cage door. When they joined him, he threw the door closed and bolted it.

8 'Toby!' they screamed. 'What are you doing?'

9 'If the tigers are out there,' Toby gulped, 'we should be safe in here.'

10 Realisation dawned on the others as they understood what a smart piece of thinking that was.

1 What part of speech is 'enclosure'? (paragraph 1)
A adjective
B noun
C verb
D adverb
E preposition

2 What mistake had Rod and Betty made at the zoo? (paragraph 1)
A they got lost
B they fed the tiger the wrong food
C they lost the keys to the tiger cage
D they left the tiger enclosure open
E they went to get the zoo keeper

3 What part of speech is 'Tim'? (paragraph 2)
A common noun
B proper noun
C collective noun
D pronoun
E abstract noun

4 Why did Toby start crying? (paragraph 3)
A he was worried about the tiger
B he was worried about his other friends
C he was hungry
D he wanted to see the tiger
E he thought the tiger might attack them

5 Why is the silence described as 'unnerving'? (paragraph 4)
A it makes it easier to hear the tiger
B it makes the children feel nervous because it's too quiet
C it makes it easier for the tiger to find the children
D they should be able to hear Rod and Betty
E they should be able to hear the zoo keepers

6 'Quivering' is what part of speech? (paragraph 6)

A collective noun
B proper noun
C adverb
D adjective
E verb

7 Which word tells us that it took a long time for Toby to reach the tiger's cage? (paragraph 6)

A eternity
B terrified
C reached
D direction
E pointed

8 What part of speech is 'pair'? (paragraph 7)

A proper noun
B concrete noun
C collective noun
D abstract noun
E common noun

9 Why did the children tiptoe across to the cage? (paragraph 7)

A they didn't want the tiger to hear them
B they wanted to sneak up on Toby
C they didn't want the other children to hear them
D they were playing a game
E they didn't want to get their feet dirty

10 'Smart' is what part of speech? (paragraph 10)

A noun
B verb
C adverb
D adjective
E conjunction

LESSON 12 PART 3: ANSWER SHEET

Mark your answer by putting a horizontal line in one of the boxes as in the example below.

Example:

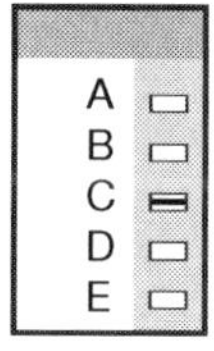

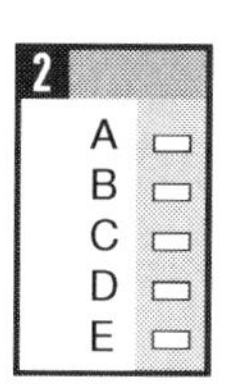

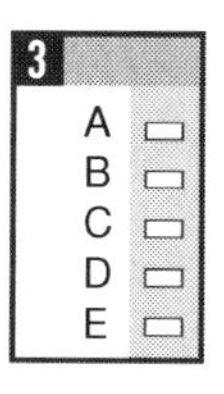

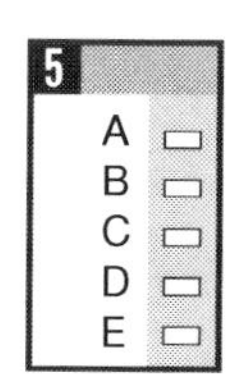

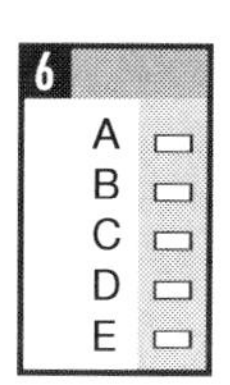

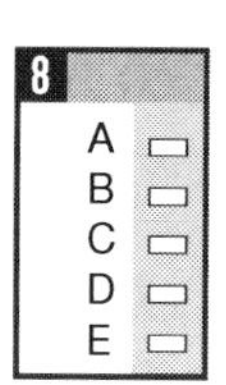

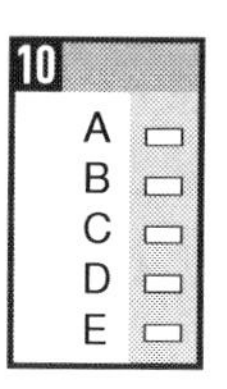

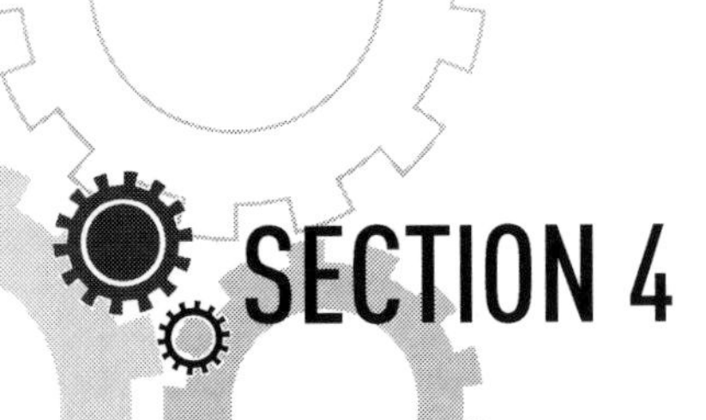

SECTION 4

LESSON 13 Improving Your Spelling Skills

In this exercise again you'll be looking at words that are spelled incorrectly and words that are misused. Let's look at some final examples.

Word	Meaning	Clue
stationery	Writing materials such as paper, pencils etc.	Remember that 'e' stands for envelope which is a type of stationery.
stationary	At a standstill.	
poor	To be bad at something or not rich.	
pour	What we do with liquids.	
hire	When someone is chosen to do a job or when you rent something.	
higher	Something that is above something else.	It's the comparative of 'high'.
hair	The stuff on your head!	Remove the first letter – your hair is in the air!
hare	An animal like a rabbit but has bigger ears and can run faster.	
wail	Cry out in pain.	It has 'ai' in the middle like pain.
whale	Large marine mammal.	
Wales	The country.	It has no 'h' and always has a capital letter as it is a proper noun.

You know how to tackle this type of question now so crack on and see how well you can do. The questions can include words we've studied already as well as some which we haven't, but which you should know. Here's another example to remind you what you need to do.

Example

Colin was happily playing with his knew toy. None

A	B	C	D	E
Colin was	happily playing	with his	knew toy.	None

In the sentence above you can see that the word 'knew' is used incorrectly since it should be 'new'. This word is in the group labelled D so you need to mark D on your answer sheet.

If we believed that all the words were used correctly you would mark E which is under the word 'None'.

LESSON 13 PART 1

My Time

My Score

Now look at the questions below. Work out where there are misspellings or correctly spelled but wrongly used words. Then mark your answer (the letter A, B, C or D) on the answer grid. If you think there are no mistakes in a particular line then mark option E on the answer grid. You have 10 minutes to complete this test.

The office: part 1

1 Martha works in an office. Her job is to higher new people to — A B C D — None E

2 help with the work their. She needs people to answer the — A B C D — None E

3 telephones, collect the post and order new stationary. The — A B C D — None E

4 more work that the new members off staff carry out, the — A B C D — None E

5 hire their pay. Martha has a lot of responsibility and works — A B C D — None E

6 extremely hard. Last week there was a heavy rein storm and — A B C D — None E

7 the office roof began to leak. Water poored in all over the — A B C D — None E

8 plaice and Martha had to make sure the roof was fixed! So — A B C D — None E

9 she nos how busy it can get. Next month Martha will take a — A B C D — None E

10 well-earned holiday. She is looking forward too it. — A B C D — None E

LESSON 13 PART 1: ANSWER SHEET

Mark your answer by putting a horizontal line in one of the boxes as in the example below.

Example:

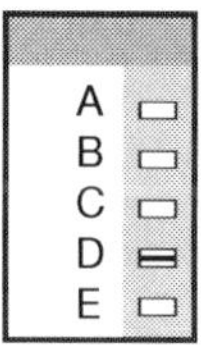

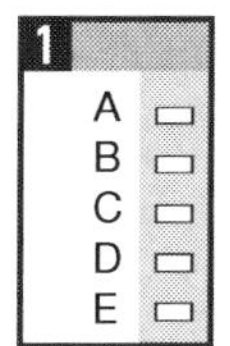

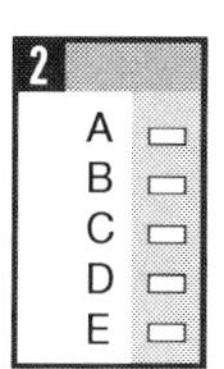

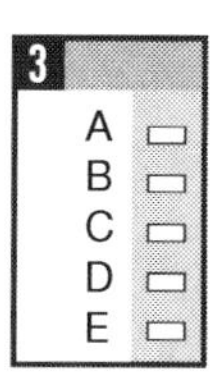

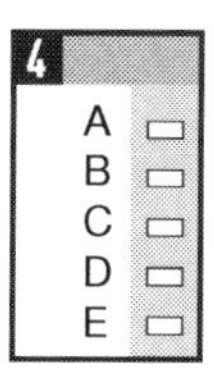

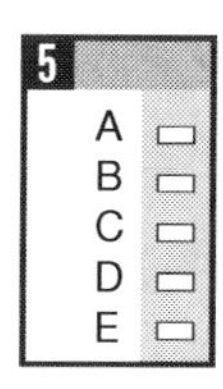

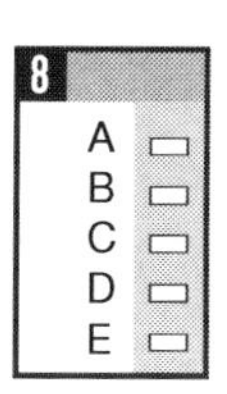

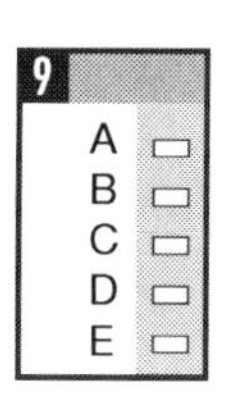

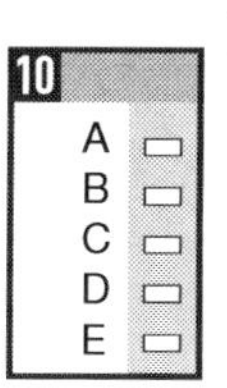

How Did You Do? Let's Find Out!

Here are the correct answers. You may mark your answers to these questions yourself. I've written the answer letter, the word that was spelled incorrectly or wrongly used and the correct spelling or word in brackets so you can follow and understand why that answer is right.

1 D higher (hire)

2 B their (there)

3 D stationary (stationery)

4 C off (of)

5 A hire (higher)

6 D rein (rain)

7 C poored (poured)

8 A plaice (place)

9 A nos (knows)

10 D too (to)

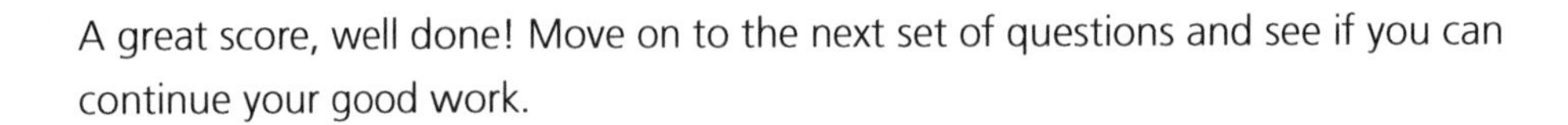

If you scored 8 or more out of 10

A great score, well done! Move on to the next set of questions and see if you can continue your good work.

If you scored 5 to 7 out of 10

This isn't a bad score but read this advice with an adult before moving on to the next set of questions.

- ➪ Look at the answers. You should know all of the words and understand when to use them. If you don't, go back and look at the spelling skills tables on pages 4, 34, 64 and 94 and use it to learn them!
- ➪ Did you notice that many of the questions contained words that were used in the wrong context? This counts as a spelling mistake and you need to choose the part of the sentence that includes that word as your answer.
- ➪ Make sure you read the entire sentence not just one line – that way you'll understand the context and hopefully know which word is being used incorrectly.

If you scored fewer than 5 out of 10

This is quite a low score so let's work hard to improve it. Read the advice above and below before moving on to the next set of questions.

Do you understand what you have to do? If not, ask an adult to read the instructions with you and make sure you understand the question type.

LESSON 13 PART 2

My Time

My Score

Now let's try some more. Work out where there are misspellings or misused words and mark your answer (the letter A, B, C or D) on the answer grid. If you think there are no mistakes in a particular line then mark option E. You have 10 minutes to complete these. Ask an adult to mark these for you.

The office: part 2

	A	B	C	D	None E
1	However, she	knows that	when she returnes	from her break	
2	she will have	a larger work	load sinse she	will need to	
3	catch up on all	that she mist	while she was	absent. Maybe	
4	she will have	to hire	a greater number	of staff on a	
5	temperary basis	to cover the	extra work. For	now though,	
6	Martha is trieing	to make sure	that everyone	knows what	
7	their asignments	are while she	is away. In	that way, the	
8	busy office	should continue	to run like	clockworke and her	
9	staff will not	need to try to	contact her wen	she is trying to	
10	relax! Hopefully	her plan will	run smoothely	while she's away.	

LESSON 13 PART 2: ANSWER SHEET

Mark your answer by putting a horizontal line in one of the boxes as in the example below.

Example:

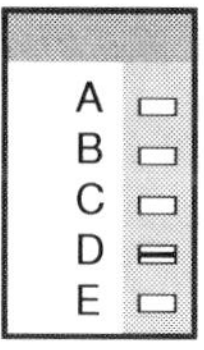

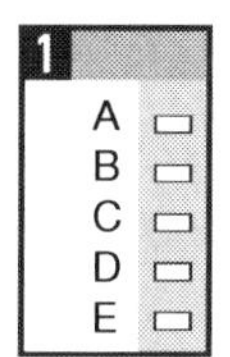

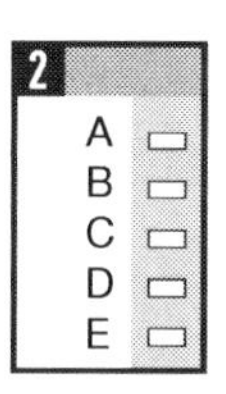

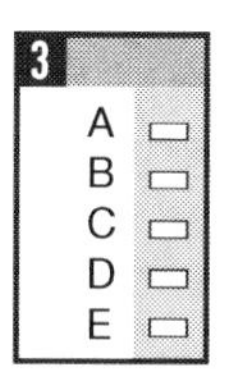

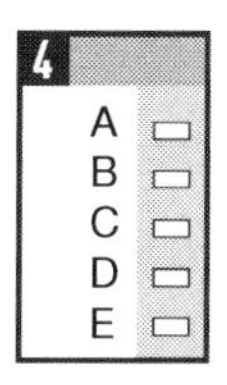

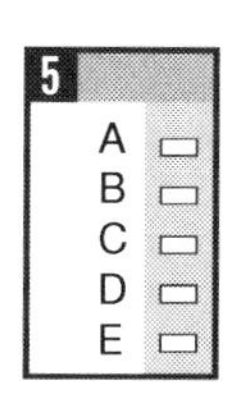

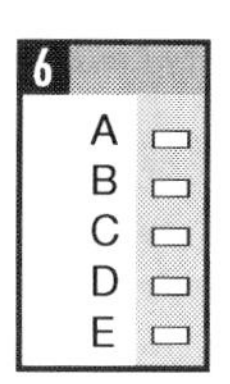

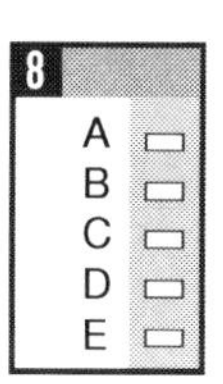

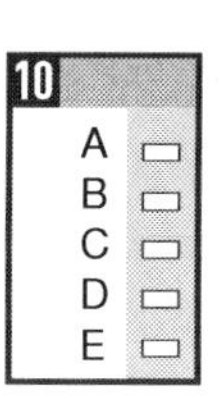

LESSON 14 Understanding Sentence Structure

Having completed lessons 2, 6, 8 and 10 you know how to answer the questions in this exercise. But I've given an example again just in case you need reminding! Look at the example and then move on to the questions.

Example

The otters splashed | playfuly | playful | playfully | playing | playefully | in the river.

playfuly	playful	playfully	playing	playefully
A	B	C	D	E

The correct answer is playfully so you would mark C on your answer sheet.

LESSON 14 PART 1

My Time

My Score

Now look at the questions below. Work out which one of the words in the boxes will complete each sentence so that it makes sense. Then mark your answer (the letter A, B, C, D or E) on the answer grid. You have 10 minutes to complete these.

The space port: part 1

1 High up, out near the [stars (A) | stares (B) | stairs (C) | starrs (D) | staires (E)], the space

2 [stashun (A) | stacion (B) | station (C) | stasion (D) | staytion (E)] turned slowly in space.

3 Its lights shone [britely (A) | brightely (B) | britly (C) | brightly (D) | brytely (E)] and

4 could be [sceen (A) | scene (B) | sean (C) | seene (D) | seen (E)] from far away. Many

5 spaceships from other [wurlds (A) | worleds (B) | worlds (C) | wolds (D) | woulds (E)]

6 often docked [their (A) | thare (B) | there (C) | they're (D) | thear (E)] to stock up on

7 supplies and fuel. There [where (A) | weir (B) | wear (C) | whir (D) | were (E)] many kinds

8 of spacecraft [to (A) | two (B) | too (C) | tow (D) | toe (E)]. They all had to remain

9 [stashunry (A) | stationery (B) | stationary (C) | stayshunary (D) | staysionary (E)] while they

10 visited this [speshul (A) | spashul (B) | spaciale (C) | special (D) | specil (E)] place.

LESSON 14 PART 1: ANSWER SHEET

Mark your answer by putting a horizontal line in one of the boxes as in the example below.

Example:

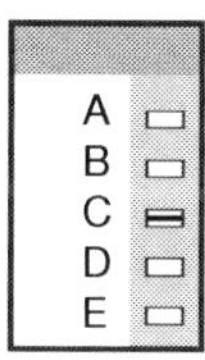

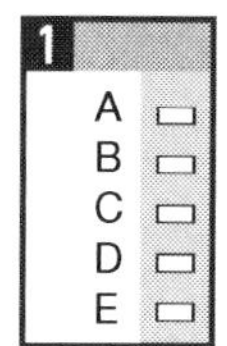

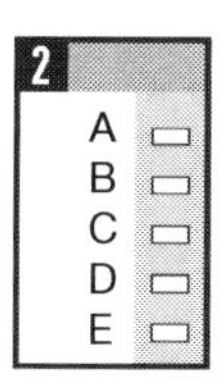

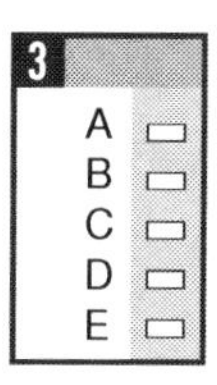

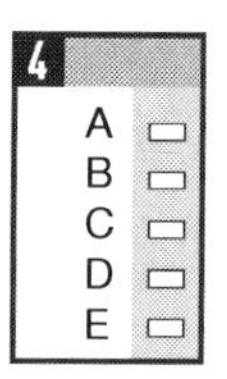

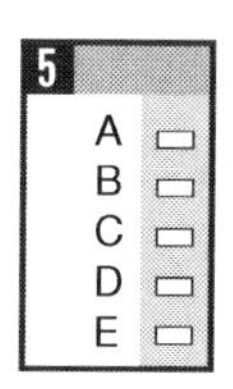

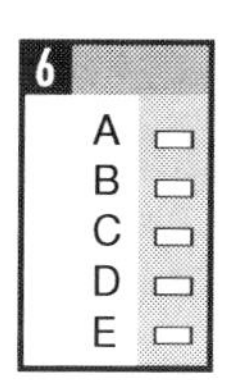

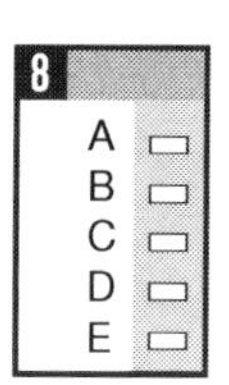

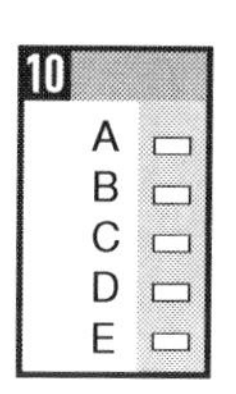

How Did You Do? Let's Find Out!

Here are the correct answers. You may mark your answers to these questions yourself. The answer letter and word are included so you can fully understand what the right answer is.

1	A	stars
2	C	station
3	D	brightly
4	E	seen
5	C	worlds
6	C	there
7	E	were
8	C	too
9	C	stationary
10	D	special

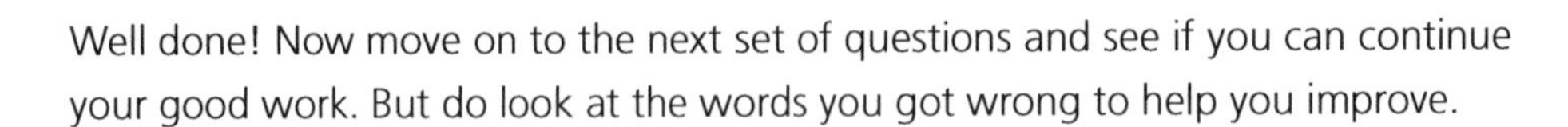

If you scored 8 or more out of 10

Well done! Now move on to the next set of questions and see if you can continue your good work. But do look at the words you got wrong to help you improve.

If you scored 5 to 7 out of 10

Read this advice with an adult before moving on to the next set of questions.

Look at the answers. You should recognise all of the words and know when they should be used. If you don't, go back and look at the spelling skills tables on pages 4, 34, 64 and 94. If they aren't on the spelling tables then use the vocabulary builder on page 125 to write the words down and look them up in a dictionary so you'll know them in future.

If you scored fewer than 5 out of 10

This is a low score so you'll need to do some work to improve. Read the suggestions above and below before moving on to the next set of questions.

Do you understand what you have to do? If not, ask an adult to read the instructions and go through the example with you again. Then take another look at your answers and see if you can correct them.

LESSON 14 PART 1

My Time

My Score

Now look at the questions below. Work out which one of the words in the boxes will complete each sentence so that it makes sense. Then mark your answer (the letter A, B, C, D or E) on the answer grid. You have 10 minutes to complete these.

The space port: part 1

1 High up, out near the stars (A) / stares (B) / stairs (C) / starrs (D) / staires (E), the space

2 stashun (A) / stacion (B) / station (C) / stasion (D) / staytion (E) turned slowly in space.

3 Its lights shone britely (A) / brightely (B) / britly (C) / brightly (D) / brytely (E) and

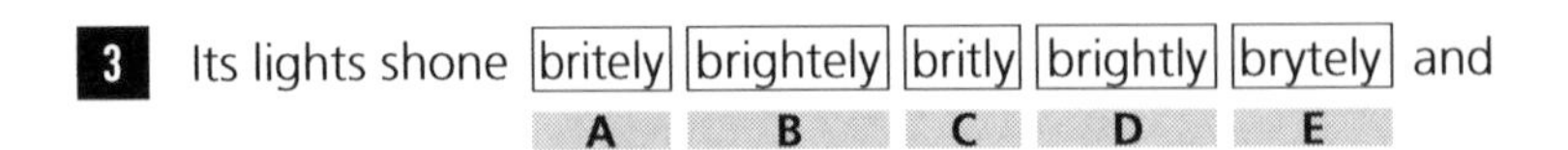

4 could be sceen (A) / scene (B) / sean (C) / seene (D) / seen (E) from far away. Many

5 spaceships from other wurlds (A) / worleds (B) / worlds (C) / wolds (D) / woulds (E)

6 often docked their (A) / thare (B) / there (C) / they're (D) / thear (E) to stock up on

7 supplies and fuel. There where (A) / weir (B) / wear (C) / whir (D) / were (E) many kinds

8 of spacecraft to (A) / two (B) / too (C) / tow (D) / toe (E). They all had to remain

9 stashunry (A) / stationery (B) / stationary (C) / stayshunary (D) / staysionary (E) while they

10 visited this speshul (A) / spashul (B) / spaciale (C) / special (D) / specil (E) place.

LESSON 14 PART 2: ANSWER SHEET

Mark your answer by putting a horizontal line in one of the boxes as in the example below.

Example:

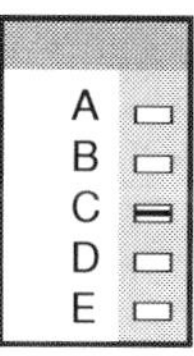

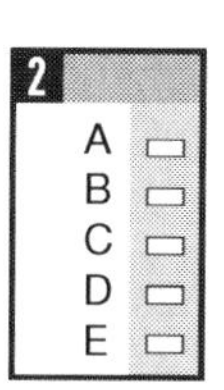
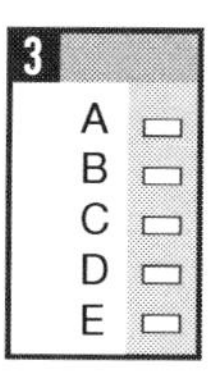

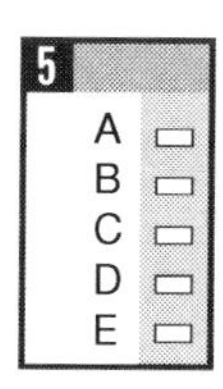

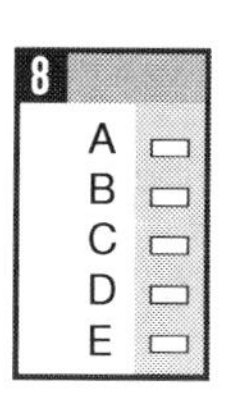
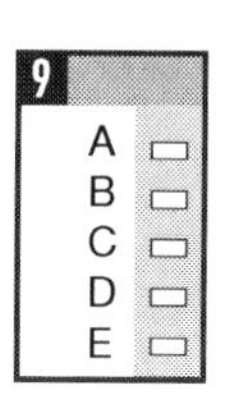
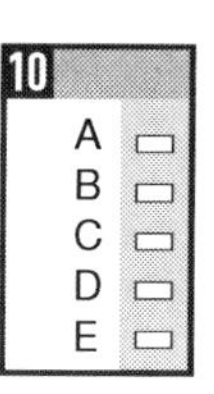

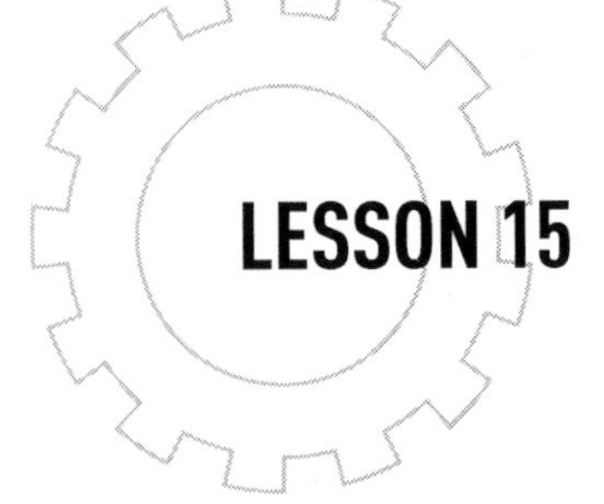

LESSON 15 Improving Your Punctuation Skills: Speech Marks

In this exercise you'll need to spot the punctuation errors in each question. To do this correctly you'll need to have a good understanding of the basic rules of punctuation and when they apply. We shall now look at quotation marks or speech marks which are used to indicate speech.

First let's think about when we use speech marks – this is very important and we have to get it right.

We use speech marks in our writing to show when words are actually being spoken. Typically there will be a verb before, in the middle or at the end of the words that are spoken. If you see the word 'that' after the verb be careful because this tells us the words aren't actually being spoken – they are simply what was said. This is sometimes called reported speech. Let's have a look at some examples.

Example 1

Sam said, 'We should go home.'

In the sentence above the speech marks go around the words which are spoken, which are: 'We should go home'. The words before this phrase tell us who said them.

Example 2

Sam said that we should go home.

In the sentence above, there are no speech marks because Sam isn't actually saying the words. Instead someone else is telling us what he said. Notice the word that, which I've underlined. This is a big give away that the words are being reported and not actually spoken.

The rules

Now we know when to use speech marks, let's look at how to use them.

Let's go though the rules – you must learn them all and apply them both in your writing and when you are looking for punctuation errors.

1. Only the words that are actually spoken are put inside the speech marks.
2. The words being spoken always start with a capital letter, unless they are continuing a sentence which has been split by the verb telling us who is speaking.
3. If we are told who is speaking before the actual words, place a comma immediately after the verb.
4. If we are told who is speaking after the actual spoken words, place a comma immediately after the last word but inside the speech marks.
5. If there is a question mark or exclamation mark after the spoken words, a comma isn't needed.

Phew! Now learn all of those rules. If you're not sure what some of them mean, look at the examples below. I've told you which rules are being used in each example. I've also underlined the punctuation.

Example 3

Bill said, 'I like eating strawberries.'

In the sentence above, use rules 1, 2 and 3.

Example 4

'I like eating strawberries,' said Bill.

In the sentence above, use rules 1, 2 and 4.

Example 5

'I like,' said Bill, 'eating strawberries.'

In the sentence above, use rules 1 and 2.

Example 6

'Do you like strawberries?' asked Bill.

In the sentence above, use rules 1, 2 and 5.

LESSON 15 PART 1

My Time

My Score

Now look at the questions below. Work out where capital letters, full stops, question marks, apostrophes, commas and inverted commas have been omitted and mark your answer (the letter A, B, C or D) on the answer grid. If you think there is no mistake in a particular line then mark option E on the answer grid. You have 10 minutes to complete this test.

The café: part 1

1 Robert met his friend clarence at the café one day. It was the — A B C D — None E

2 usual time for them to meet. they enjoyed chatting about this — A B C D — None E

3 and that and reading their books When Robert arrived — A B C D — None E

4 he saw Clarence was already there. 'hello Clarence,' he said — A B C D — None E

5 as he sat down, 'would you like a cup of tea' Clarence looked — A B C D — None E

6 up from his newspaper and replied 'That would be lovely.' — A B C D — None E

7 Robert went up to the counter and returned with two steaming — A B C D — None E

8 cups of tea and a plate of chocolate biscuits. he set them down — A B C D — None E

9 and asked, 'Whats that story about that you're reading?' — A B C D — None E

10 'Oh,' answered Clarence, 'it's about a singing dog! — A B C D — None E

LESSON 15 PART 1: ANSWER SHEET

Mark your answer by putting a horizontal line in one of the boxes for each answer below.

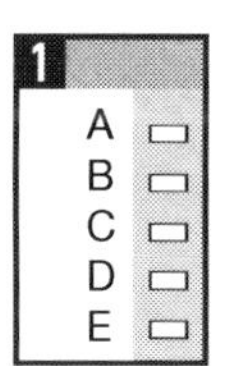

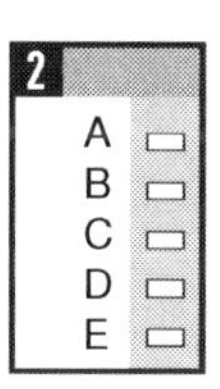

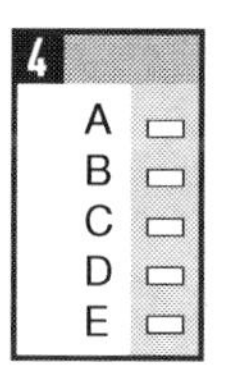

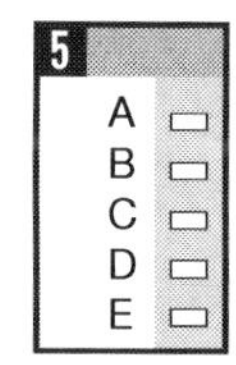

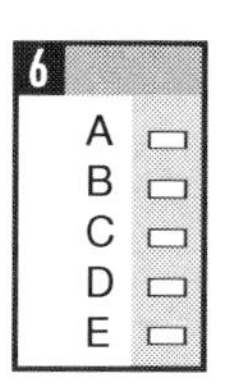

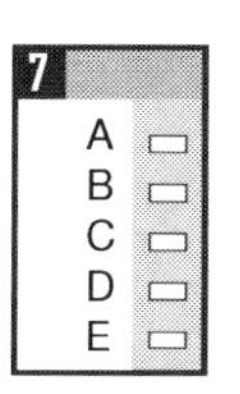

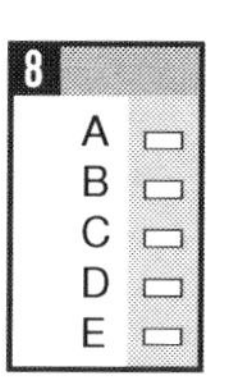

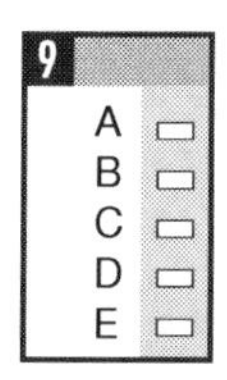

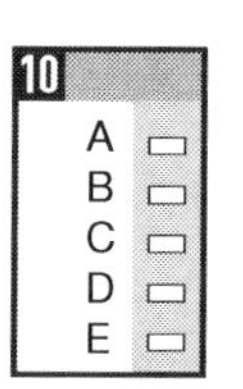

How Did You Do? Let's Find Out!

Here are the correct answers. You may mark your answers to these questions yourself. I've written the right answer letter and the example of punctuation or capital letters just so you know!

1	B	Clarence
2	C	They
3	C	books.
4	C	'Hello
5	D	tea?'
6	C	replied,
7	E	none
8	D	He
9	B	'What's
10	D	dog!'

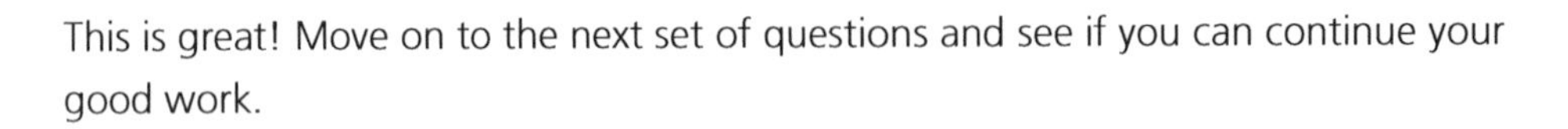

If you scored 8 or more out of 10

This is great! Move on to the next set of questions and see if you can continue your good work.

If you scored 6 or 7 out of 10

This score could be improved. Make sure that you read complete sentences and take a lot of care when thinking about where punctuation and capital letters should go.

If you scored 5 or fewer out of 10

Let's work hard to get a better score in part 2. Read the suggestions below before moving on to the next set of questions.

➪ If any instuctions are unclear ask an adult to explain them. Then take another look at your answers and see if you can correct them.

➪ Make sure you really understand all the places where full stops and capital letters should be used. You must be strong on these before you move on.

➪ Read each sentence and look for those which ask questions. That way you'll know when to put in a missing question mark.

➪ Work out exactly which words are being spoken – put your speech marks around them and then all the punctuation that goes with them. Make sure you understand all the different rules for speech marks.

LESSON 15 PART 2

My Time

My Score

Now let's try some more. Work out where capital letters, full stops, question marks, apostrophes, commas and inverted commas have been omitted and mark your answer (the letter A, B, C or D) on the answer grid. If you think there is no mistake in a particular line then mark option E on the answer grid. You have 10 minutes to complete this task. Ask an adult to mark your answers for you.

The café: part 2

	A	B	C	D	None
1	Robert couldn't	believe it	'Did you say a singing	dog?' he	E
2	asked incredulously.	Yes,' said	Clarence, 'I know	it's hard to	E
3	believe but	its actually really good!'	He put	his bookmark in	E
4	the book and	closed it. Then	he handed it to	his friend. robert	E
5	took it from	him and flipped	the book over	and read the	E
6	summary on the	back. he began	laughing as he	read it. 'This	E
7	sounds hilarious'	he said to	Clarence who	nodded in	E
8	agreement. 'Where	did you find	it' asked	Robert. Clarence	E
9	told his friend	that he had	been looking through	the old books	E
10	in the library	and it was	on sale. what a great	find it had been!	E

LESSON 15 PART 2: ANSWER SHEET

Mark your answer by putting a horizontal line in one of the boxes for each answer below.

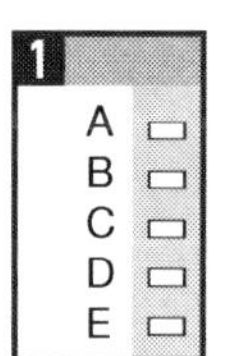

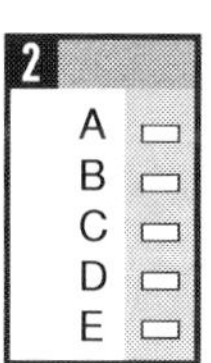

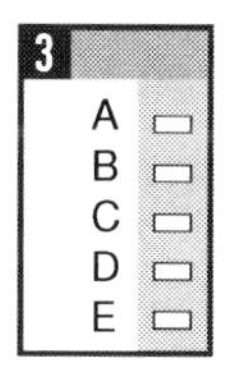

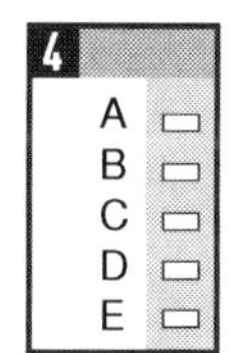

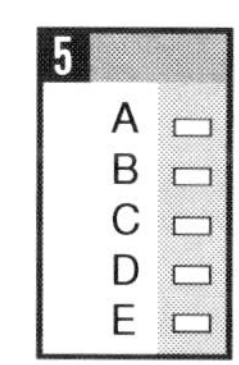

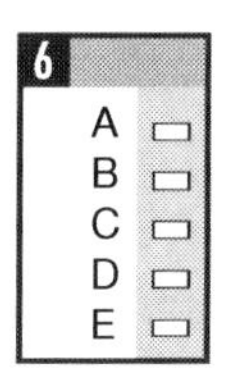

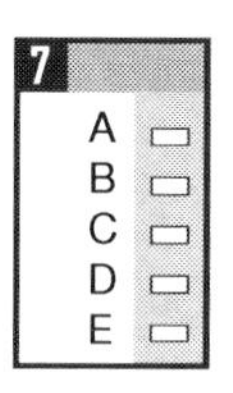

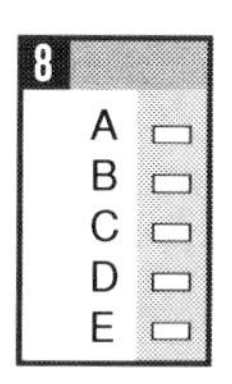

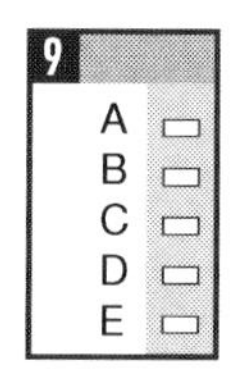

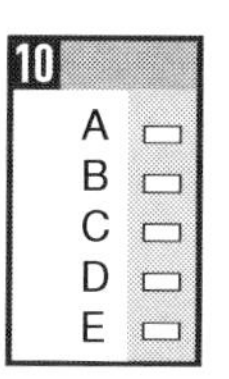

LESSON 16 Practising Comprehension and Grammar

In this exercise you'll read a passage of text and then answer some questions about it. Remember that you'll be asked a mixture of comprehension and grammar questions.

A Improving Your Comprehension: Inferential Questions

Let's look at questions which ask you to identify specific words from the passage. Some of the most difficult questions to answer are those which require you to use your skill of inference.

Inference is what we do when we aren't given some information directly. Instead, we look at the information we do have and try to work out additional information from it.

Let's look at an example.

Example

Arnold headed towards the bookcase. It was dusty and covered in cobwebs. Reaching through them, Arnold's fingers trembled as he fumbled with a hidden catch.

1 How do you think Arnold was feeling?

A happy
B upset
C nervous
D angry
E annoyed

The answer to the question above is C – nervous. Although the passage doesn't actually tell us this, we can infer it from the information that's given to us – that Arnold's fingers were trembling.

Questions for comprehension skills follow the next part of this lesson, which is on grammar skills.

B Improving Your Grammar: Verbs

In this exercise you'll be asked questions concerning grammar. Here you'll tackle some of the more common types which you'll need to make sure you know really well. For this lesson we'll look at verbs and some of their forms.

Verbs are action or doing words.

Example

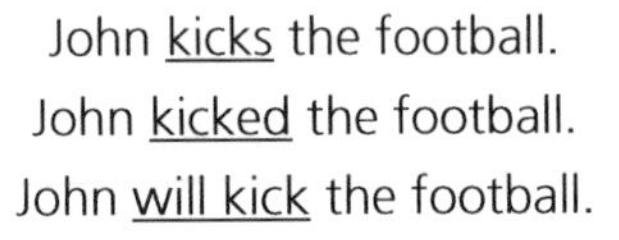

John <u>kicks</u> the football.
John <u>kicked</u> the football.
John <u>will kick</u> the football.

In the three sentences above, three simple tenses of the verb 'to kick' are shown.

By tense we mean at what time things happen.

The present tense: This tells us about what is happening now. 'John kicks...'

The past tense: This tells us about something that has happened and is finished. 'John kicked...'

The future tense: This tells us about something that will happen. 'John will kick...'

Watch out for these tenses of verb when trying to work out what part of speech a word is.

Now look at the sentences below. See if you can work out which word or words in each sentence are verbs and underline them.

1. The dog chewed on a bone.
2. There is a new restaurant in town and it serves wonderful food.
3. Today the rain will fall heavily then the sun will come out.
4. White clouds gather over London but not Manchester.
5. The squirrel climbed the tree and held some nuts in its mouth.

Answers: 1. chewed, 2. is, serves, 3. will fall, will come, 4. gather, 5. climbed, held

LESSON 16 Practice Questions

My Time

My Score

Now read the passage below carefully and answer the questions that follow. They may be comprehension or grammar questions. Additionally, there may be questions about things you learned in lessons 4, 8 and 12. When you've worked out the correct answer, mark its letter on the answer grid on page 123. Ask an adult to mark your answers for you. You should be able to complete these in about 10 minutes, which includes the time you have to read the passage.

The warehouse

In the excerpt that follows, detective Bob Stubbs is on the trail of some sinister characters who have hidden in a local warehouse.

1 The weather turned from overcast to plain awful as Bob strode off the main street and into one of the many smaller alleys that spread like the strands of a spider's web through this part of town.

2 As he pulled his collar up and fastened the remaining buttons on his overcoat, the rain which had threatened, finally fell in large, cold drops. He shuddered as he stepped over a rapidly forming puddle and pressed as close as he could to the tall brick buildings which seemed to look down upon him with interest.

3 As he turned the shadowy corner, Bob crouched down ever so slightly and skulked towards an innocent-looking, stout, metallic container. He paused to catch his breath and observe the warehouse across the street. It looked deserted, quiet – almost derelict, yet Bob was sure he could hear sinister sounds coming from within.

4 His breathing became heavier as a 'clank-clunking' noise echoed down the street and two broad and heavy-looking, cast-iron doors groaned outwards towards him. From deep within emerged two rough-looking men with thick dark eyebrows and scowls that would turn milk sour.

5 But what were they up to? As Bob continued to observe from his hiding place the two men looked furtively about before slipping off down the street out of view.

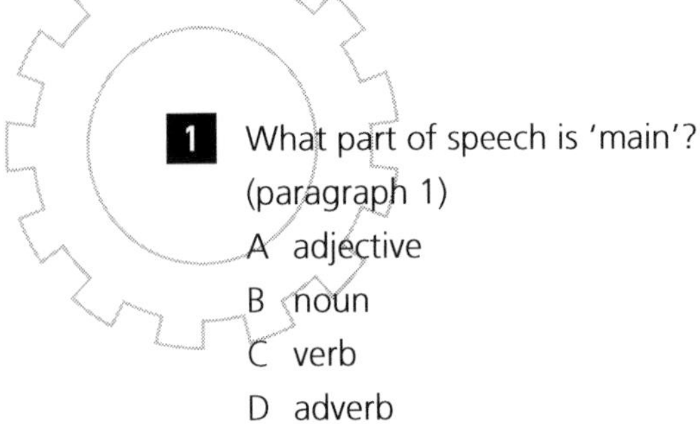

1 What part of speech is 'main'? (paragraph 1)
A adjective
B noun
C verb
D adverb
E preposition

2 'Spread' is an example of? (paragraph 1)
A collective noun
B adverb
C adjective
D common noun
E verb

3 'Rapidly' is what part of speech? (paragraph 2)
A adjective
B noun
C verb
D preposition
E adverb

4 Why did Bob shudder? (paragraph 2)
A he was scared
B he was brave
C he was cold and wet
D he was angry
E he was upset

5 'Skulked' is what part of speech? (paragraph 3)
A noun
B adverb
C adjective
D verb
E pronoun

6 'Derelict' is what part of speech? (paragraph 3)
A noun
B verb
C adverb
D adjective
E preposition

7 What made the 'clank-clunking' noise? (paragraph 4)
A two rough-looking men
B detective Bob Stubbs
C sour milk
D two cast-iron doors
E two dark eyebrows

8 What part of speech is 'echoed'? (paragraph 4)
A verb
B adverb
C noun
D adjective
E proper noun

9 Which word suggests the men did not want anyone to know what they were doing? (paragraph 5)
A continued
B observe
C hiding
D view
E furtively

10 What part of speech is 'continued'? (paragraph 5)
A noun
B verb
C adverb
D adjective
E conjunction

LESSON 16 PART 3: ANSWER SHEET

Mark your answer by putting a horizontal line in one of the boxes as in the example below.

Example:

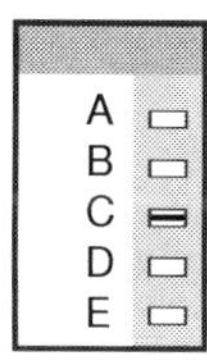

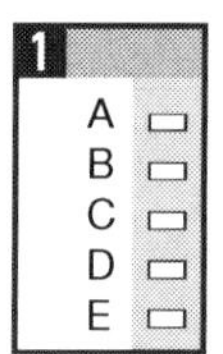

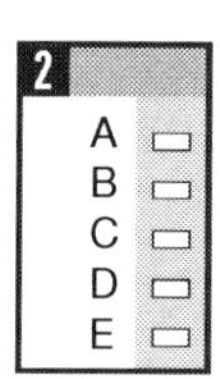

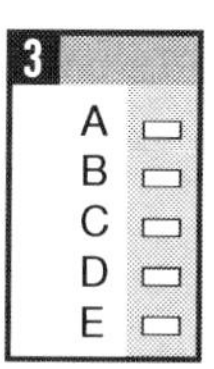

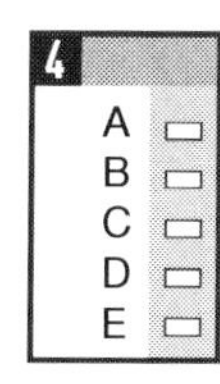

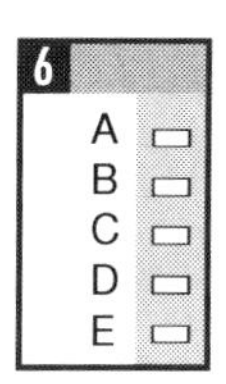

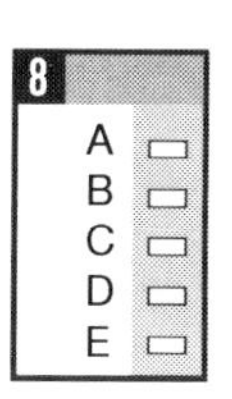

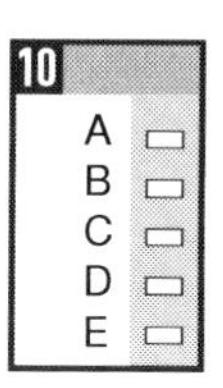

SCORE SHEET

Use the score sheets below to track your scores. You'll be able see which areas you're strong at and which you'll need to practise further.

LESSON	Part 1	Part 2
1 – Spelling		
5 – Spelling		
9 – Spelling		
13 – Spelling		
LESSON	**Part 1**	**Part 2**
2 – Sentence structure		
6 – Sentence structure		
10 – Sentence structure		
14 – Sentence structure		
LESSON	**Part 1**	**Part 2**
3 – Punctuation		
7 – Punctuation		
11 – Punctuation		
15 – Punctuation		
LESSON	**Practice questions**	
4 – Practising comprehension and grammar		
8 – Practising comprehension and grammar		
12 – Practising comprehension and grammar		
16 – Practising comprehension and grammar		

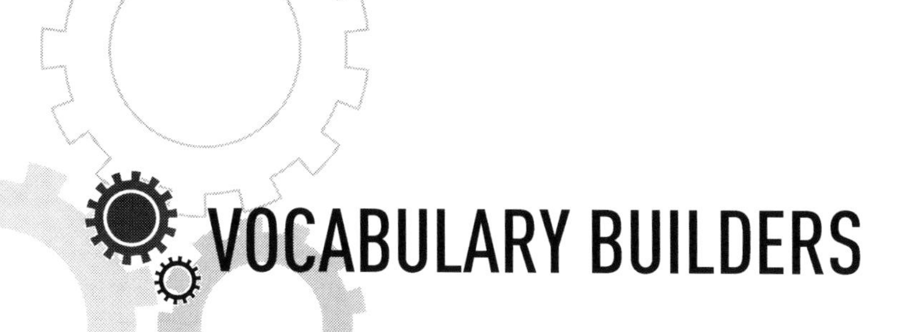

VOCABULARY BUILDERS

New words

Use this table to write down any new words you've come across in this book. Use a dictionary to look up the meaning of each so that you'll know what they mean in future.

New word	Meaning

Proper nouns

Now read something which you haven't been given in school, such as a book or a magazine. List all of the proper nouns you come across in the table below and try to put them in a category (see page 21).

Category	Proper noun 1	Proper noun 2

Which category had the most proper nouns?

____

AND FINALLY...

Let me begin by saying 'well done!' You must have worked hard to complete this book, especially on top of your homework from school.

Now that you've completed the first English book in the *Practise & Pass 11+* series, it's time to take stock. Have a look back at your scores and work out which questions you found quite straightforward and scored well on, and which ones you found tougher and didn't score so well on.

Make sure you read back over the methods for each question – these will serve you well during your examination. When you're ready, move on to the next book in the series (*Practise & Pass 11+ Level Two: Develop English*), which will feature more of all these questions. In that book I'll also show you more examples of sentence structure and punctuation, and will give you more spelling for you to practise and learn.

And don't forget, if you need help with non-verbal reasoning, mathematics or verbal reasoning, there are books for each of those to help you prepare for your exams.

- *Practise & Pass 11+ Level One: Discover Maths*
- *Practise & Pass 11+ Level One: Discover Non-Verbal Reasoning*
- *Practise & Pass 11+ Level One: Discover Verbal Reasoning*
- *Practise & Pass 11+ Level Two: Develop English*
- *Practise & Pass 11+ Level Two: Develop Maths*
- *Practise & Pass 11+ Level Two: Develop Non-Verbal Reasoning*
- *Practise & Pass 11+ Level Two: Develop Verbal Reasoning*
- *Practise & Pass 11+ Level Three: Practice Test Papers*

Keep working and good luck!

ANSWERS

LESSON 1: part 2

1. C becomeing (becoming)
2. D ancsious (anxious)
3. D beleive (believe)
4. A Suddenley (Suddenly)
5. C cowerd (cowered)
6. D echowing (echoing)
7. E none
8. A reconised (recognised)
9. B movment (movement)
10. D forrest (forest)

LESSON 2: part 2

1. A was
2. B what
3. B straight
4. E they
5. C would
6. B had
7. B wait
8. A to
9. A carried
10. D so

LESSON 3: part 2

1. C Cork.
2. D Trott
3. A Then
4. A Blewitt
5. C Mr
6. D He
7. E none
8. A Then
9. E none
10. D soon.

LESSON 4

1. D gnarled and cracked
2. B adjective
3. D worn and uneven
4. B noun
5. E kneeling
6. E adjective
7. B adjective
8. E a tattoo
9. A proper noun
10. C his captain

LESSON 5: part 2

1. E none
2. A tern (turn)
3. C hoped (hopped)
4. D of (off)
5. C emereged (emerged)
6. C leappt (leapt)
7. B wonderfull (wonderful)
8. E none
9. D replyed (replied)
10. A scarred (scared)

LESSON 6: part 2

1. B When
2. D sat
3. E were
4. D their
5. A while
6. C passed
7. E had
8. D could
9. A wailing
10. D to

LESSON 7: part 2

1. A Carl
2. A computer.
3. C I've
4. B it's
5. C exciting'.
6. E none
7. B Eventually
8. D happily.
9. D Gareth
10. B it's

LESSON 8

1. D because the stone looked out of place in the cattle shed
2. D adjective
3. E adjective

4. C whether or not to take the cattle into their shed
5. A adverb
6. C noun
7. B adjective
8. C he wanted to see how long it would be before it rained
9. E adjective
10. E noun

LESSON 9: part 2

1. B finnish (finish)
2. B victourious (victorious)
3. B beeds (beads)
4. B sharpely (sharply)
5. E none
6. C approche (approach)
7. E none
8. C heroe (hero)
9. A shye (shy)
10. D delite (delight)

LESSON 10: part 2

1. D building
2. C saw
3. E sea
4. D digging
5. A were
6. A would
7. C pair
8. D high
9. B came
10. D saved

LESSON 11: part 2

1. B guard's
2. A flag.
3. B that?'
4. D 'That's
5. C 'It's
6. A As
7. D fields,
8. E none
9. C it,
10. D sea.'

LESSON 12

1. B noun
2. D they left the tiger enclosure open
3. B proper noun
4. E he thought the tiger might attack them
5. B it makes the children feel nervous because it's too quiet
6. D adjective
7. A eternity
8. C collective noun
9. A they didn't want the tiger to hear them
10. D adjective

LESSON 13: part 2

1. C returnes (returns)
2. C sinse (since)
3. B mist (missed)
4. E none
5. A temperary (temporary)
6. A trieing (trying)
7. A asignments (assignments)
8. D clockworke (clockwork)
9. C wen (when)
10. C smoothely (smoothly)

LESSON 14: part 2

1. A looked
2. E point
3. A stared
4. C light
5. D pace
6. E which
7. E too
8. D bay
9. A was
10. B for

LESSON 15: part 2

1. B it.
2. B 'Yes
3. A believe,
4. D Robert
5. E none
6. B He
7. A hilarious,'
8. C it?'
9. E none
10. C What

LESSON 16

1. A adjective
2. E verb
3. E adverb
4. C he was cold and wet
5. D verb
6. D adjective
7. D two cast-iron doors
8. A verb
9. E furtively
10. B verb

Printed in Great Britain
by Amazon